EDGE

NO. 5

TABLE OF CONTENTS

Your favorite series, from the beginning. Just a click away.

www.comicsontheweb.com

The years of peace are at an end for the August Empire of Shinacea. From within, dark forces threaten the serenity of the Imperial City. From without, enemies from the steppes gather beyond the walls of civilization.

In these turbulent times, lost amidst events far larger than himself, lives a common thief of uncertain parentage named Boon Sai Hong. His home is the city of Zhumar, a walled fortress on the Empire's frontier.

The story of this humblest of lives would be as a single grain lost in a sandstorm but for a series of events that lead Boon to the possession of ancient objects with the power to change the world.

And so,
our tale begins...

Chuck
DIXON
WRITER

Jeff
JOHNSON
PENCILER

Tom
RYDER
INKER

Chris
GARCIA
COLORIST

Dave
LANPHEAR
LETTERER

"It is the wise man
who can discern
good fortune from ill."

Wing Tei Sun

THE FRONTIER CITY OF ZHUMAR, FAR TO THE WEST OF THE COMFORTS AND PLEASURES OF THE IMPERIAL COURT.

A FORTRESS BUILT HARD BY THE ENDLESS STEPPES.

HOME TO ONE HUNDRED THOUSAND HAPLESS SOULS WHO LIVE EACH DAY BENEATH THE SHADOW OF A TARTAR'S SWORD.

YOU'LL HAVE NO *NEED* OF THIS RING IN HELL.

NO AMOUNT OF GOLD WILL BUY YOU MERCY *THERE.*

Uh— TIGHT.

Uh?

-- AND HE HAS TOLD NO ONE OF THESE DISCOVERIES?

FATHER TRUSTS NO ONE BUT YOURSELF.

THE RING IS A SOURCE OF GREAT *WORRY* TO HIM, PRINCESS ZHENG.

IT SHOULD BE IN THE HANDS OF A *WARRIOR* NOT A SCHOLAR, TEI SU.

AND *MORE* SO THE BOOK. HE WOULD NOT TELL ME HOW HE CAME TO--

FATHER!

MURDERED. AND THE RING IS GONE.

BUT THERE IS NO MARK ON HIM. DEATH TOOK HIM WITHOUT STRUGGLE.

IT WAS NOT *DEATH* THAT TOOK YOUR FATHER, TEI.

IT WAS *FEAR.* LOOK AT HIS EYES.

EH?

THEY HAVE GAZED INTO THE *HEART* OF HORROR.

AI!

WHAT MIGHT HAVE FRIGHTENED HIM SO? HE WAS ALONE IN HIS LIBRARY WITH HIS BOOKS.

ALONE?

I AM NOT SO CERTAIN.

YOU MUST ALLOW ME TO PLAY ONE *MORE* ROUND; TO SPARE MY HONOR.

THE PRIZE YOU HAVE WON IS TOO *DEAR* TO LOSE.

THE FIRST *LESSON* OF GAMBLING, MERCHANT FONG.

NEVER WAGER WHAT YOU CANNOT BEAR TO SACRIFICE.

MERCY, HONORABLE X'AIN!

MERCY!

I EXPECT DELIVERY TO MY HOUSE *BEFORE* DAWN...

...TO *SPARE* YOUR "HONOR."

I HATE A POOR LOSER. HE WOULD CROW LIKE A COCK HAD HE WON.

AS *REMOTE* A POSSIBILITY AS THAT WOULD BE.

NOW HE CRIES FOR PITY WHEN FORTUNE TURNS ITS BACK.

MAY WE TURN NOW TO MORE *SERIOUS* MATTERS, X'AIN?

NOTHING IS MORE SERIOUS THAN HONOR AND CHANCE, NUBOTAI.

YOU HAVE PROMISED MY MASTER THE RING OF STAFFS. I HAVE BEEN HERE *THREE* DAYS AND MY HANDS ARE EMPTY.

IT IS *WITHIN* MY GRASP. I HOPE YOUR KHAN RECALLS *HIS* PROMISES AS WELL AS YOU DO *MINE*.

THE DEAL YOU STRUCK WITH HIM IS *MEANINGLESS* WITHOUT THE RING TO SEAL IT.

IT *WILL* BE HERE. I HAVE SENT MY BEST MEN TO RETRIEVE IT. ONLY THE LIFE OF A FEEBLE *BOOKWORM* STANDS IN MY WAY.

SHOULD HE BE DISAPPOINTED, THE KHAN'S *WRATH* IS AS GREAT AS HIS GENEROSITY.

I *TOLD* YOU...

Eh?

AND?

VENERABLE JUSTICE -- I HAVE COME FROM THE HOME OF THE SCHOLAR WING TEI.

WE *FAILED* TO OBTAIN THE RING. *PRINCESS ZHENG* WAS THERE AND--

AND A *THIEF* -- HE STOLE THE RING AND ESCAPED.

ZHENG MAI? THAT *WITCH?*

I WOULD DO *ANYTHING* TO EXPUNGE MY SHAME.

DID YOU *HEAR* THAT, NUBOTAI?

I *DID,* JUDGE.

A *MINOR* SETBACK. NOTHING TO CONCERN *US*.

I AM NOT CONCERNED.

YOUR VEILED THREATS GROW *TIRESOME*.

I WILL *HAVE* THE RING BEFORE DAWN.

NOW *LEAVE* ME. I MUST *FIND* THIS THIEF AND BRING THE *FULL* WEIGHT OF IMPERIAL LAW UPON HIS HEAD.

AS YOU *WISH*.

A COMMON THIEF--

"-- I WONDER IF HE *KNOWS* WHAT HE HAS CALLED DOWN UPON HIMSELF."

Uh! Uh!

DAMN!

NGGGG--

GET-- OFF!

WHY-- WON'T--IT-- MOVE?

COULD IT BE YOUR FAT PEASANT FINGERS AND NOT THE RING?

WHO SPEAKS?

STEP INTO THE LIGHT AND FACE ME!

I AM HERE, STUPID.

HERE. IN THE CAGE BENEATH THESE FILTHY DUCKS.

AND PUT THAT *DAGGER* AWAY!

AAAH!

AS YOU CAN SEE, I CAN'T *HURT* YOU.

OOF!

IDIOT.

THAT RING IS NO SILLY BAUBLE. IT IS AN OBJECT OF *GREAT* POWER.

AND *YOU*-- THE GODS *ALONE* KNOW WHY-- WERE CHOSEN TO WEAR IT.

YA! I CANNOT HEAR A DEMON-MONKEY SPEAKING TO ME YA YA...

STOP THAT *YAMMERING!*

THIS IS *IMPORTANT!*

GET ME OUT OF THIS CAGE BEFORE--

BOON SAI HONG...THE FABLED JADE RAT.

WONDERFUL. *MORE* IDIOTS.

HANA!

BOSS TIGER RECEIVES NO TRIBUTE. HE SENT YOU FOR THE PHOENIX HEART AND YOU *VANISH*.

THE BROTHERHOOD OF SCOUNDRELS *DEMANDS* PAYMENT.

UNNH!

A FAILURE EVEN AS A THIEF.

WHY *ME*?

YOU WILL PAY IN GOLD OR BLOOD, BOON. NO MATTER TO *ME*.

I HAVE HAD ILL LUCK THESE PAST NIGHTS. THE HEART WAS NOT THERE. ONLY AN UGLY SCROLL AND THIS RING.

BUT I CAN'T *PRY* IT FROM MY HAND.

THEN BOSS TIGER WILL HAVE THE RING *AND* YOUR FINGER.

BLOOD *AND* GOLD.

WAIT! WE COULD TRY *BUTTER!*

OR *GOOSEFAT!*

HOLD *STILL!*

YOU *HAVE* NINE MORE!

OOP!

Uh?

THE *RING* --

YOU *SEE?* IT IS --

-- CURSED?

I AM *SORRY,* TEI SU.

IT IS *FITTING,* PRINCESS ZHENG.

FATHER'S TREASURED LIBRARY DIED *WITH* HIM.

BUT FOR *ONE* BOOK.

THE BOOK OF THE HELL OF THE HUNGRY DRAGONS. FATHER NEVER LET ME OPEN IT. IT IS *MORE* THAN PAPER AND INK.

TO VIEW IT IS TO SEE FUTURE DAYS.

DAYS OF SUCH TERROR THAT *SIGHT* OF THEM TOOK YOUR FATHER'S *LIFE.*

TO HAVE SUCH AN ARTIFACT *AND* THE RING OF STAFFS STOLEN BY A COMMON THUG.

I MUST FIND THIS THIEF WHILE THE SKY IS STILL DARK AND THE CITY'S GATES ARE BARRED.

SHOULD HE ESCAPE, THEN WE SHALL *ALL* BE CONSUMED BY THE HORROR YOUR FATHER FORESAW.

I SHALL *REMAIN,* PRINCESS ZHENG--

WHAT SWEETER WAY TO BEGIN THE MORNING THAN WITH THE *WINNINGS* OF THE NIGHT BEFORE.

OBLIGATION *BEFORE* PLEASURE, JUDGE.

YOU *BORE* ME, NUBOTAI.

LIKE A NOISOME *RAIN*.

MY POWER OVER THIS CITY IS *UNQUESTIONED*.

I *WILL* HAVE THIS THIEF *AND* WHAT HE STOLE IF I MUST BURN EVERY HOUSE WITHIN THESE WALLS TO *ASH!*

YOUR ZEAL WILL NOT BE *UNREWARDED*. WHEN THE KHAN COMES TO POWER THIS CITY WILL REMAIN YOURS.

YOU WILL RULE WITH A HAND ALL YOUR *OWN*. NOT THE SUZERAINTY GRANTED YOU AT THE WHIM OF THE EMPEROR.

I LOOK *FORWARD* TO THAT JOYOUS DAY.

ESTEEMED JUSTICE X'AIN, A GIFT FROM THE MERCHANT FONG.

AH. IT HAS *ARRIVED*.

UNROLL IT QUICKLY. I WOULD *GAZE* UPON ITS DELIGHTS.

I WAS *UNAWARE* OF YOUR INTEREST IN CARPETS, X'AIN.

SOMETIMES YOU *AMUSE* ME, NUBOTAI.

THE CARPET IS MERE *BAGGAGE*.

IT IS *ENOUGH* SHAME TO LOSE ONE'S DAUGHTER ON A BET.

IT WOULD BE NEEDLESSLY CRUEL TO COMPOUND HIS DISHONOR BY PARADING HER THROUGH THE MARKET CROWD.

I *KNOW* HE CAME THIS WAY.

A MEMBER OF THE CRIME GUILD. A THIEF.

I DO NOT LIKE WHAT I SEE TONIGHT.

THE CITY IS *ALIVE* WITH SPIRITS AND EVIL OMENS. I FEEL IT IN MY BONES.

IT IS *AGE* YOU FEEL.

YOU SAY YOU *KNOW* THIS THIEF?

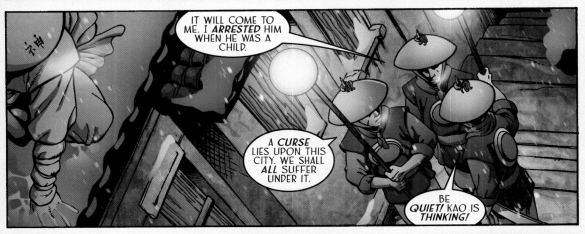

IT WILL COME TO ME. I *ARRESTED* HIM WHEN HE WAS A CHILD.

A *CURSE* LIES UPON THIS CITY. WE SHALL *ALL* SUFFER UNDER IT.

BE *QUIET!* KAO IS *THINKING!*

HE IS AN ORPHAN. RAISED BY BOSS TIGER. A SKILLED BURGLAR.

HIS NAME IS... IS...

...BOON SAI HONG.

...THE JADE RAT!

...BOON SAI HONG.

IN THE BEGINNING...

The First were the creators of the universe before their descent into a constant state of war. Their leader Altwaal ended the war with the creation of the Eidolon rift, a tear in reality which separated their home, Elysia, into two Houses connected by a single gate. Peace and boredom followed. Now the First have been catalyzed into action with the appearance of the Sigil-Bearers, beings of great power that rivals theirs. A Sigil-Bearer has even dared to kill one of their kind. If these Sigil-Bearers can destroy the First, are the First truly gods?

HOUSE SINISTER

HOUSE DEXTER

House Sinister's Leader, **Ingra**, wants to take over House Dexter and reunite the two Houses under her rule. Her daughter **Persha** is seeking Altwaal, the first Leader of all First, hoping to convince him to return and reunite the Houses. Her power amplified by Altwaal's Gauntlet, Persha mentally connects with her father **Pyrem**, Dexter's Leader, instead. He's being held prisoner in Braag's keep, having been captured in the Eidolon rift by an army of House Dexter and Sinister insurrectionists led by **Seahn**, who has made allies of Ingra and Braag. Ingra visits Pyrem, unable to keep away from the man she loves above all others, but her love is hidden beneath her taunts. **Trenin** and **Yala** plan a private raid to free their Leader from House Sinister, hoping to avoid war. Seahn gleefully anticipates the war he believes he has begun, but his euphoria fades when he realizes his closest friends are sneaking away. As Persha tries again to find Altwaal, she makes contact with all possible versions...

Barbara **KESEL** WRITER

Andrea **DI VITO** PENCILER

Rob **HUNTER** INKER

Rob **SCHWAGER** COLORIST

Dave **LANPHEAR** LETTERER

WYTURE--

--THERE'S BEEN PROGRESS.

SEAHN HAS TAKEN THE FIRST STEP ON AN IRREVOCABLE TRAIL TOWARD WHAT MUST BE.

HOW FARES YOUR CHARGE?

PERSHA HASN'T YET FOUND WHAT SHE'S SEEKING.

SHE'S LOOKING FOR ALTWAAL AMONG ALL THE VISIONS, DREAMS AND SIGHTINGS SHE'S DRAWN IN THROUGH HER AMPLIFIED SIGHT.

IT'S *HIM*.

WYTURE, I'VE FOUND HIM!

I'VE GOT TO GO *SEE* HIM! THE GAUNTLET BINDS ME TO HIS LOCATION AND THE SHADOWS WILL TAKE ME THERE.

ARE YOU CERTAIN HE *WANTS* TO BE FOUND?

ALTWAAL IS THE FINEST OF THE FIRST! HOW COULD *HE* REFUSE US IN THIS TIME OF NEED?

AS YOU WILL.

ENSON, IT HAS *TRULY* BEGUN.

THE FATE THAT WILL BRING OUR TWO TOGETHER AND TEST THEM BOTH.

YOU SEEM SMUG, WYTURE.

YOU ASSUME YOURS WILL PREVAIL.

DON'T MAKE THE MISTAKE OF UNDERESTIMATING SEAHN.

ENSON!

THE BONDS ARE WEAKENING-- BRAAG'S CONCENTRATION MUST HAVE BROKEN!

THAT'S NOT ALL I'LL BREAK.

SNAPPT

I'M SICK OF THE FIGHTING...CAN'T WE JUST GO HOME?

NO! NOT WHILE OUR LEADER IS IMPRISONED!

NOT WHILE HE NEEDS US! YALA! WE'RE HERE WITH YOU!

"--TRENIN'S GOT SOME ANGER TO SHARE!"

SHIELD YOUR EYES, GRACOS--

PYREM, WHERE'S ALTWAAL'S GAUNTLET?

GONE.

STOLEN.

BY HIS EYES! HOW--

AH, NO MATTER. LET'S GET YOU AWAY FROM HERE--

"-- BEFORE YALA GETS SO DRUNK ON BATTLE THAT SHE DECIDES TO TAKE ON INGRA."

INGRA'S HERE?

MORE REASON WHY WE SHOULD NOT BE.

EVERYBODY JUST CALM DOWN!

NOBODY'S LEAVING!

SO SPEAKS THE LEADER TO BE.

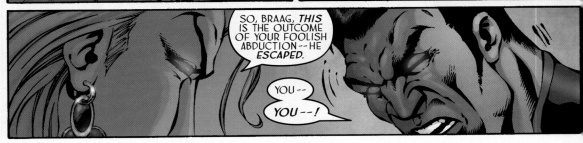

SO, BRAAG, THIS IS THE OUTCOME OF YOUR FOOLISH ABDUCTION--HE ESCAPED.

YOU--

YOU--!

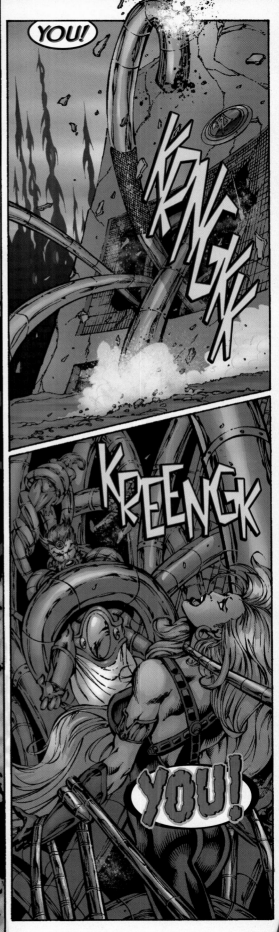

INGRA, HIS BLOOD IS ON *YOUR* HANDS!

GRACOS?

VIHAM?

NO! LET IT NOT BE!

NOOO...

Indeed, I fear the cost to all First should be phenomenal...

...but the truth cannot be changed by wishing ourselves back to an innocent state.

Reality must be borne, not denied.

So have I been compelled back here, to the world of enigmatic beings of an age before time.

Inserting myself invisibly into the midst of their daily lives...

I observed a scene of patient communion between enemies — reluctant interrogator and stoic subject reaching the accord of silence.

The prisoner piqued my curiosity, for his true nature was not instantly made plain to my perceptions.

As I pushed to unearth the facts of his existence, a shadowy title for the entirety of his kind came forth...

...the Negation.

A name weighted with bilious enlightenment...

...followed by the vision of a sickening symbol that spells the further erosion of all I know...

There is not simply, beyond we First, a secondary source of power...

...but another universe!

One whose forces could engulf our own.

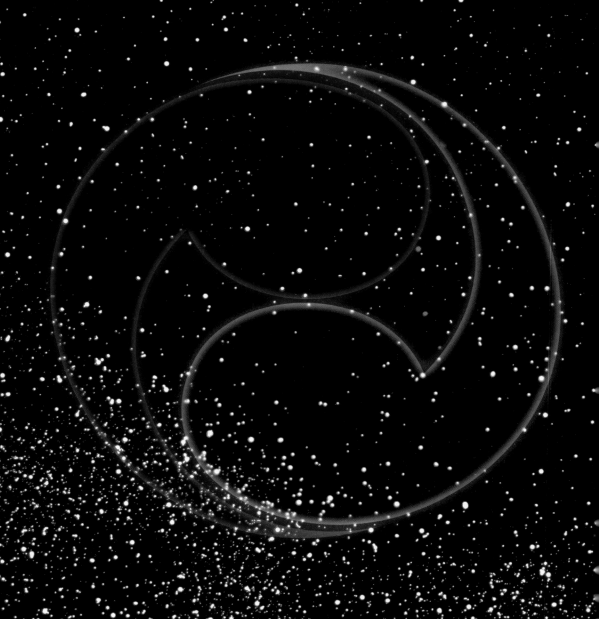

Chapter 18
by

Barbara
KESEL
WRITER

Andrea
DI VITO
PENCILER

Rob
HUNTER
.INKER

Rob
SCHWAGER
COLORIST

Dave
LANPHEAR
LETTERER

WHAT *IS* THIS?

THERE'S *FIVE* OF THEM AND THIS FIGHT ISN'T *OVER?*

DON'T TELL ME I PICKED THE WRONG HOUSE.

NO.

YOU'RE EXACTLY WHERE YOU SHOULD BE--

TRENIN.

--AND I KNOW EXACTLY WHAT YOU *NEED.*

OH?

AND THAT WOULD BE *WHAT?*

YOUR MOTIVES ARE AN ENIGMA TO ME, ENSON--

--WHAT HAVE YOU DONE TO THEM?

WE'VE JUST STEPPED BETWEEN MOMENTS.

EVERYTHING WILL BE ALL RIGHT.

I JUST NEED YOU TO *LISTEN*.

TRUST ME.

TRUST...

TALK.

YOU KNOW MY AIMS ARE BENEVOLENT.

YOU AGREED TO TRUST ME ONCE.

I NEED THAT *TRUST* TO CONTINUE.

NOT AS FAR AS *SEAHN*.

YOU'RE MAKING A MISTAKE, PROTECTING HIM.

I MADE A *BIGGER* MISTAKE LONG AGO, LETTING HIM LIVE.

SEAHN HAS HIS PURPOSE, TRENIN. HE OR THE OTHER WILL--

OTHER?

STOP.

RETURN US TO NORMAL-- *NOW!*

I DON'T WANT TO HEAR ANY DEFENSE OF THAT TROUBLEMAKER--

THEN I HAVE COME FOR NOTHING.

PERHAPS...

...BUT IF IT WERE *MY* TASK TO FIND THIS MAN AND I HAD NO SUCCESS...

...I'D WONDER IF I COULDN'T DO THE JOB MYSELF!

I'M SORRY I COULDN'T GIVE YOU THE ANSWER YOU WERE *EXPECTING,* PERSHA.

I HOPE YOU ARE ABLE TO FIND THE LEADER YOU SEEK.

SO DO I, *AYDEN.*

THANK YOU...FOR YOUR KIND COUNSEL.

I'LL LEAVE YOU TO YOUR PEACE NOW.

FAREWELL.

OH! I NEVER INTRODUCED MYSELF...

...BUT I SEE YOU KNOW MY NAME.

SO...

...THERE MAY BE HOPE.

ALWAYS...

MYSTIC™

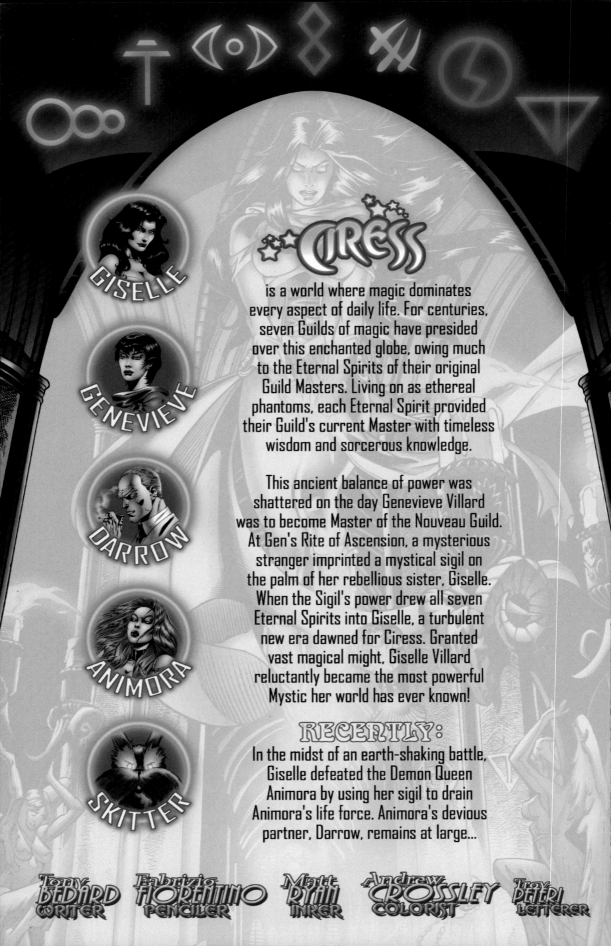

CHAPTER 21

CIRESS

CIRESS is a world where magic dominates every aspect of daily life. For centuries, seven Guilds of magic have presided over this enchanted globe, owing much to the Eternal Spirits of their original Guild Masters. Living on as ethereal phantoms, each Eternal Spirit provided their Guild's current Master with timeless wisdom and sorcerous knowledge.

This ancient balance of power was shattered on the day Genevieve Villard was to become Master of the Nouveau Guild. At Gen's Rite of Ascension, a mysterious stranger imprinted a mystical sigil on the palm of her rebellious sister, Giselle. When the Sigil's power drew all seven Eternal Spirits into Giselle, a turbulent new era dawned for Ciress. Granted vast magical might, Giselle Villard reluctantly became the most powerful Mystic her world has ever known!

RECENTLY:

In the midst of an earth-shaking battle, Giselle defeated the Demon Queen Animora by using her sigil to drain Animora's life force. Animora's devious partner, Darrow, remains at large...

GISELLE

GENEVIEVE

DARROW

ANIMORA

SKITTER

Tony **BEDARD** Writer

Fabrizio **FIORENTINO** Penciler

Matt **RYAN** Inker

Andrew **CROSSLEY** Colorist

Troy **PETERI** Letterer

NO.

IT'S NOT MURDER IF A SOLDIER DEFENDS HER COUNTRY.

ANIMORA THREATENED THE *WORLD.*

YOU CAME THROUGH, 'ELLE. YOU *SAVED* US ALL.

FWOOSH

?

Um...

YOU'RE THE MAGIC EXPERT, GEN. ARE THEY *SUPPOSED* TO GO UP IN SMOKE ONCE THEY'RE DEAD?

I *GUESS* SO. I DON'T KNOW. I'VE NEVER MET ANYTHING *LIKE* ANIMORA BEFORE.

HOPE I *NEVER* DO AGAIN.

JUST... JUST LEAVE ME *ALONE* FOR A WHILE...

ARE YOU ALL RIGHT? I DIDN'T *SINGE* YOU, DID I?

NO, DARROW. YOUR TIMING WAS IMPECCABLE. DO YOU THINK THEY *BOUGHT* IT?

YES. THE TELEPORT EFFECT BLENDED WITH THE COLOR OF THE FLAME SPELL. I EVEN LEFT A SCORCH-MARK ON THE GROUND SHAPED LIKE YOU--

PLEASE. EVEN WHEN I'M FEELING GOOD, I CAN'T STOMACH YOUR BOASTING...

WHAT ABOUT GISELLE? SHOULDN'T WE FOLLOW HER?

NO NEED. SHE'S RIGHT *HERE,* WHENEVER I NEED HER.

FOR NOW, LET HER GO *HOME...*

"...SARGE BLOCKED OFF THE BACK OF THE ALLEY."

SETTLE DOWN, KIDS. I'M NOT MUCH FOR EXERCISE. SO WHAT SAY WE CUT OUT THE RUNNIN' AND JUST HAND OVER THE BAG, NICE AND SLOW?

BUTCH...?

POOF

WING IT, SMALL FRY! THAT SOUNDED SHORT-RANGE-- THEY'LL 'PORT BACK IN NEARBY...

YVES MANION, NOUVEAU P.D. BUNCO SQUAD.

I BELIEVE YOU HAVE SOMETHING THAT DOESN'T **BELONG** TO YOU.

HERE YA GO, SIR.

Hey!

GOOD EVENING, MISTER TINKLEBRIAR. ARE YOU GENTLEMEN OKAY?

It wuz a rough ride, but we'll be fine.

GOOD, GOOD. BECAUSE IF MY BEST EARNERS HAD BEEN HURT OR GONE MISSING...WELL, LET'S JUST SAY THERE'D BE *HELL* TO PAY.

...THE *PIXIE DUST LAB...*

...THEY CHURN OUT THAT POISON FOR *YOU...?!*

BUT...ALL OF THESE COPS CAN'T BE IN YOUR POCKET...

FAASH

PROTECT ME FROM MY ENEMIES!

YEAH, YEAH. I KNOW THE DRILL...

MILADY... ⇒SMAK⇐

GUY, YOU CHARMER...

GISELLE, C'MON! YOU GOTTA MEET MY NEW SWEETHEART!

YVES MANION. PLEASURE TO MEET YOU, GISELLE. LORRAINE CURSES YOUR ABSENCE SO MUCH, I FIGURE YOU MUST BE SOMETHING SPECIAL.

OOH, THIS ONE HAS MANNERS, LORRAINE. NOTHING LIKE -- WHAT WAS HIS NAME? PAOLO? YOU KNOW, THE ONE WHO GOT BUSTED --

ANCIENT HISTORY. AND WATCH WHATCHA SAY. MANION'S A COP.

IT'S ALL RIGHT. I KNOW ALL ABOUT IT. HOW D'YOU THINK LORRAINE AND I MET?

DOES HE MEAN...?

YEP. HE ARRESTED PAOLO.

WHEN THE GOOD DETECTIVE CAME TO QUESTION ME, I COULD SEE RIGHT AWAY IT WAS TIME TO TURN A NEW LEAF.

CHAPTER 22

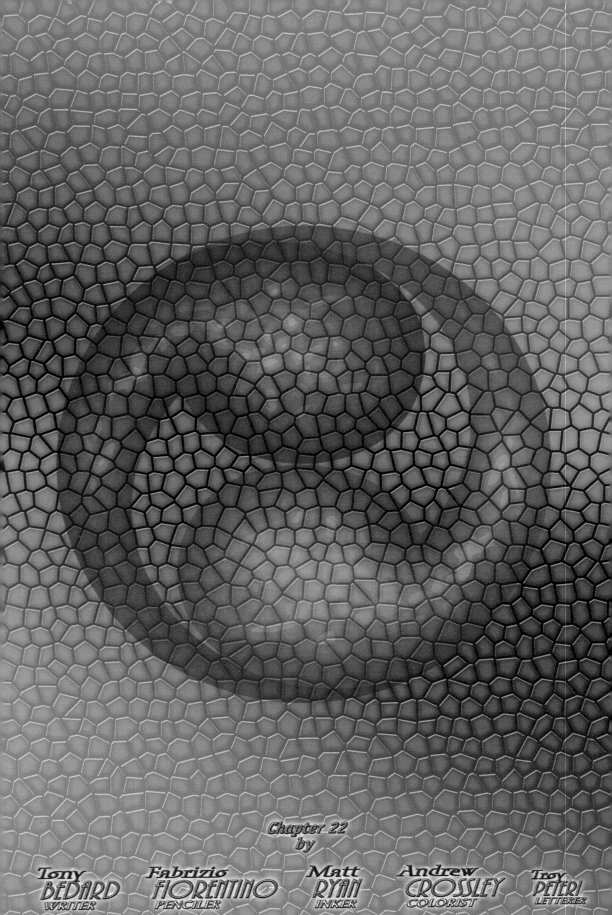

Chapter 22
by

Tony
BEDARD
WRITER

Fabrizio
FIORENTINO
PENCILER

Matt
RYAN
INKER

Andrew
CROSSLEY
COLORIST

Troy
PETERI
LETTERER

YOU *SURE* SHE'S HERE? I MEAN, WE HAVEN'T SEEN HER IN A *WEEK*, SO WHY SHOULD SHE MAKE IT EASY FOR US *NOW*?

TRUST me, kid...

GOTTA HAND IT TO YOU, 'ELLE, THIS PLACE *IS* THE LIVING END!

JUST WHEN YOU THOUGHT YOU'D *WORN OUT* EVERY CLUB IN TOWN, eh?

THIERRY!

Um...HI. IT'S GOOD TO --

HEY, GIRLS! *THIS* IS THE GUY I WAS TELLING YOU ABOUT!

THIERRY CHEVALIER...

...MEET THE BEST PARTY-PALS A GIRL EVER HAD...

...*LORRAINE*, *GUY* AND *ANNETTE!*

SEVEN SPIRITS...I HAVEN'T STAYED OUT ALL NIGHT SINCE ART SCHOOL...

CONSIDER THIS *NIGHT SCHOOL.* YOU HAVE THE VERY *BEST* PROFESSORS, DARLING. CLASS MEETS AGAIN AT MIDNIGHT. TOODLES!

I'M FAMISHED.

WANNA COME UP FOR A NIBBLE?

HONESTLY... I'D RATHER *TALK,* NOW THAT WE *FINALLY* HAVE A MINUTE TO OURSELVES. I'VE BEEN, WELL...

I'M *WORRIED* ABOUT YOU, GISELLE. YOU DISAPPEAR FOR DAYS AT A TIME, AND YOU HAVE TO ADMIT YOU'VE BEEN ACTING... *DIFFERENT.*

I *CARE* ABOUT YOU. I WANT TO KNOW IF YOU'RE—

CLAUDE, PLEASE HAIL THIS *BOY* A TAXI. AND WHILE HE'S WAITING, PLEASE *EXPLAIN* TO HIM WHAT *"DOUBLE-ENTENDRE"* MEANS.

SKITTER? ARE YOU *HERE*? I SAW YOU HANGING AROUND LAST NIGHT, BUT I LOST TRACK OF YOU AFTER WE LEFT--

THIERRY?!

WHAT IN THE INFERNAL PLANES ARE YOU AND SKITTER *DOING* HERE?

IT'S *GISELLE.* MORE TO THE POINT, IT'S THOSE HORRIBLE *PEOPLE* SHE HANGS OUT WITH--

HOLD ON...

ÈĿẐ?M¿

RATS. I DIDN'T MEAN TO VANISH THE *ICE CREAM...*

SORRY IF I RATTLED YOU, GEN. IT'S ABOUT YOUR SISTER. HAVE YOU NOTICED A *CHANGE* IN HER?

HOW SO?

WELL...SHE'S REALLY MOODY AND SELFISH. DISAPPEARS FOR DAYS AT A TIME.

STAYS OUT ALL NIGHT LONG WITH LORRAINE, GUY AND--

ANNETTE. I'VE *MET* THEM.

ACTUALLY, IT SOUNDS LIKE GISELLE IS BACK TO *NORMAL.*

NO, HONEY. THIS IS MORE SERIOUS THAN IT LOOKS.

GISELLE?

GISELLE, WE NEED TO SPEAK.

OKAY, BUT COULD YOU COME HERE FOR A CHANGE? THAT NOWHERE-PLACE YOU SPOOKS LIVE IN GIVES ME A *HEADACHE.*

IS THAT *REALLY* WHY YOU WON'T COME TO THE SPIRIT PLANE?

WHAT ARE YOU GETTING AT?

YOU'RE AVOIDING US BECAUSE YOU KNOW YOU'RE BEHAVING POORLY.

THE SELF-INDULGENT NIGHTS OUT, THE HAIR-TRIGGER TEMPER...

YOU VERY NEARLY *KILLED* THAT CONSTABLE JUST FOR STARTLING YOU.

YOU *SAW* THAT, huh?

WE SEE *EVERYTHING* YOU DO. AND I HAVE TO TELL YOU, THE OTHER GUILD SPIRITS ARE EXPRESSING DOUBTS ABOUT YOUR WORTHINESS--

SO WHAT *ELSE* IS NEW? YOU SPIRITS HAVE BEEN LOOKING FOR A WAY OUT EVER SINCE THE DAY YOU GOT STUCK WITH ME.

NOT TRUE. YOU'VE SHOWN GREAT POTENTIAL, BUT NOW YOU ARE BACKSLIDING. AND SHOULD YOU CHOOSE TO *ALLY* YOURSELF WITH THAT *CRIMINAL*...

YOU DON'T EVEN KNOW *WHY* I AGREED TO MEET WITH HIM TONIGHT.

I AM MORE CONCERNED WITH WHAT HE *WANTS* FROM YOU. WOULD HE PRESUME THAT YOU HAVE SOME *INFLUENCE* IN THE NOUVEAU GUILD WHEN YOU AREN'T EVEN A *MEMBER*?

PROBABLY NOT.

DID YOU REVEAL YOUR MYSTIC ABILITIES TO HIM IN ANY WAY?

IF YOU'RE ALWAYS WATCHING, THEN YOU *KNOW* I DIDN'T.

SOMEHOW, THIS MAN, OR SOMEONE HE ANSWERS TO, IS AWARE OF YOUR INNER DISHARMONY.

IF YOU ALLOW HIM TO FURTHER UNBALANCE YOU, DUTY WILL COMPEL US TO WITHHOLD OUR COUNSEL FROM YOU.

IT'S A *TEMPTING*, THOUGHT: TO NEVER AGAIN HEAR ALL OF YOU *YAKKING* INSIDE MY MIND. BUT YOU SHOULDN'T HAVE BOTHERED WITH THE ULTIMATUM.

I AGREED TO MEET MANION--AWAY FROM MY FRIENDS--SO THAT I COULD *DESTROY* HIM.

HE'S TRYING TO *USE* ME. AND AFTER WHAT I'VE BEEN THROUGH THE LAST FEW MONTHS, THAT'S THE *WORST* MISTAKE ANYONE COULD MAKE.

-- WHAT IN THE INFERNAL PLANES ARE *THEY* DOING HERE?!

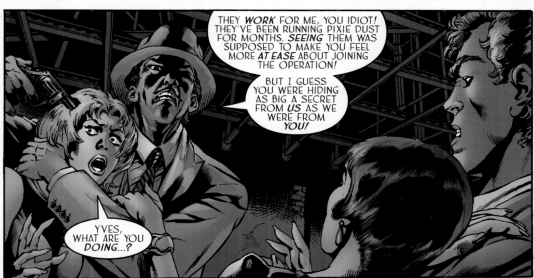

THEY *WORK* FOR ME, YOU IDIOT! THEY'VE BEEN RUNNING PIXIE DUST FOR MONTHS. *SEEING* THEM WAS SUPPOSED TO MAKE YOU FEEL MORE *AT EASE* ABOUT JOINING THE OPERATION!

BUT I GUESS YOU WERE HIDING AS BIG A SECRET FROM *US* AS WE WERE FROM *YOU!*

YVES, WHAT ARE YOU *DOING...?*

MAKING IT *HARDER* ON HIMSELF.

NO...

WHRAMM

OUR STORY SO FAR...

SAM

ROIYA

JeMERIK

ZANNIATI

TCHLUSARUD

KHYRADON

FOR CENTURIES, the five human worlds of the Planetary Union have been at war with the lizardlike Saurians of Tcharun, unable to find a weapon formidable enough to turn the tide of battle.

And then along came Sam.

A mustered-out soldier with a good heart, SAMANDAHL REY and his fellow ex-soldier ROIYA SINTOR came looking for work on the neutral world Tanipal only to be ambushed by Sam's Saurian enemy TCHLUSARUD In the ensuing battle, they picked up two crucial allies – the mysterious JeMERIK MEER (smitten by Roiya) and ZANNIATI (a spy anxious to escape the harem of Tanipal's Sultan). Victory, though, came not from any of them but rather from a strange sigil, a brand of vast power burned into Sam's chest by a vanishing stranger. In fact, Sam first realized the sigil's potential the moment Roiya was slain – and Sam, in a moment of anguished grief, neutralized the attack by unintentionally unleashing a half-mile wide explosion of matter-transforming force.

Once Sam, JeMerik and Zanni escaped Tanipal, however, an over-wrought Sam learned that all was not lost: while Roiya's lifeless body lay in stasis aboard Sam's starship, the *BitterLuck*, her mind and soul had been "uploaded" into the ship's computers seconds before her death, allowing Roiya to live on in holographic form. Now the two of them are taking point in defending the human race from the merciless Saurian army, with Sam on one side as the Planetary Union Field Commander and Khyradon, a self-styled wargod, leading the Saurians in an all-out attack on the Union.

PREVIOUSLY...

Sam has rejoined Roiya and JeMerik only to be told that Zanni has gone on the vengeance path to find and kill Sultan Ronolo. He vows to search the stars to find her. This proves unnecessary as Zanni is a prisoner on an enormous asteroid powered by Arc engines and aimed directly for the orbit of Gaia, the homeworld of the Planetary Union. Zanni will rejoin Sam riding a miles wide rock of space debris unless the Sigil-Bearer can tap into powers he only recently learned of on Demetria.

At the same time Tchlusarud has been banished to a remote prison fortress by Khyradon and his own mother, the Matriarch of Tcharun.

We join the story as the latest addition to the Saurian arsenal nears Gaia's troposphere...

Chuck
DIXON
WRITER

Scot
EATON
PENCILER

Andrew
HENNESSY
INKER

Wil
QUINTANA
COLORIST

Dave
LANPHEAR
LETTERER

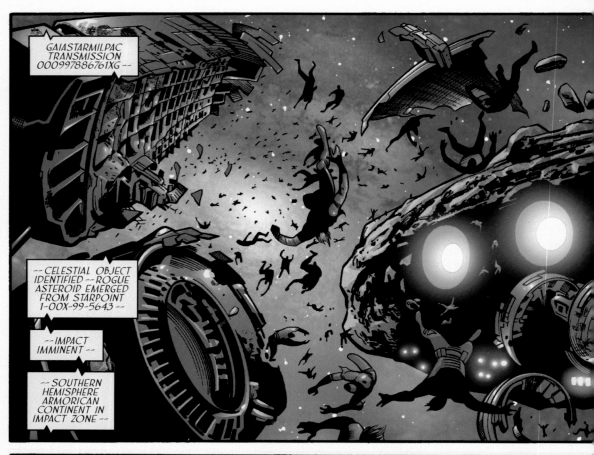

GAIASTARMILPAC
TRANSMISSION
000997886761XG --

-- CELESTIAL OBJECT
IDENTIFIED --ROGUE
ASTEROID EMERGED
FROM STARPOINT
1-00X-99-5643 --

-- IMPACT
IMMINENT --

-- SOUTHERN
HEMISPHERE
ARMORICAN
CONTINENT IN
IMPACT ZONE --

GAIASTARMILPAC
TRANSMISSION
000997886764XG --

-- ALL UNITS
PLANETARY DEFENSE TO
OFF-PLANET DEFENSE
POSTURE FIVE --

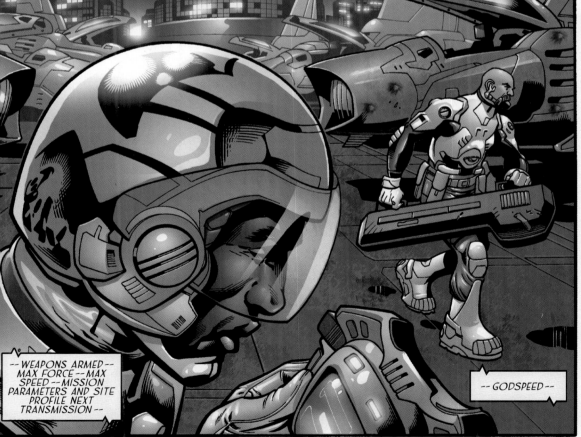

-- WEAPONS ARMED --
MAX FORCE -- MAX
SPEED -- MISSION
PARAMETERS AND SITE
PROFILE NEXT
TRANSMISSION --

-- GODSPEED --

"IT'S A *SAURIAN* INSTALLATION AND SHE'S *ALONE* ON IT."

I WON'T...

I *WON'T* DIE THIS WAY. I'LL *LIVE*, RONOLO...

...I WILL BE A *WITNESS.*

AND I'LL LIVE TO SEE YOU *SUFFER* FOR THIS.

ANY IDEA OF A *PLAN*, SAM?

WE GET US CLOSE TO THAT ROCK AND I HOP OUT AND POUND THE LIVING *HELL* OUT OF IT.

SIMPLE, DIRECT AND EFFECTIVE.

IF THAT'S MEANT TO BE SARCASM, JeMERIK...

IT'S MOMENTS LIKE THIS I *QUESTION* THE WISDOM OF ACCEPTING THE VICE PRESIDENTIAL SLOT.

BUT GANDAMAC IS DEAD AND *I'M* IN THE HOT SEAT. NOW, EVERYONE *REPORT*.

IT'S NOT A RANDOM EVENT, MADAME PRESIDENT. EARLY SCANS SHOW AN *INSTALLATION* ON THE OBJECT'S SURFACE.

ANALYSIS GIVES A STRONG INDICATION IT'S OF SAURIAN CONSTRUCTION.

IT APPEARS TO BE AN ARC DRIVE ENGINE.

PRIMARY IS *STOPPING* THIS BEAST BEFORE IT HITS OUR ATMOSPHERE. *THEN* WE THINK ABOUT REVENGE.

ADMIRAL UMPALA, ARE YOUR KIDS UP FOR THIS MISSION?

ALREADY SPACEBORNE AND PACKING *HEAT*, MADAME PRESIDENT.

AIMING POINT MINUS SIX.

ARMED

HEAVENLY MOTHER...

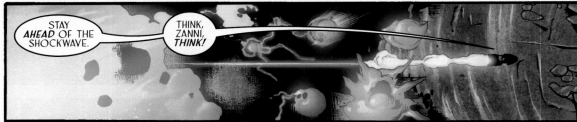

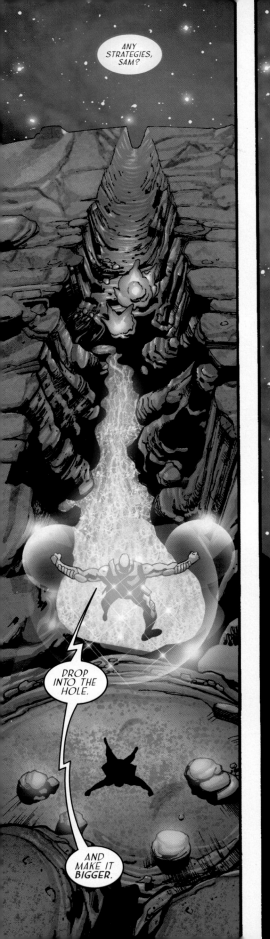
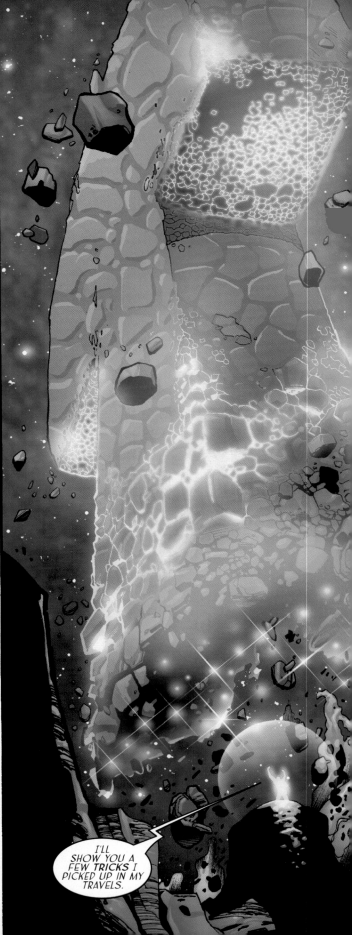

GAIASTARMILPAC TRANSMISSION 000997886901XG--

--CENTRAL ZONE'S SOUTHERN ARMORICA IN IMPACT ZONE--

--ESTIMATE 500 PLUS ASTEROID SEGMENTS 107V OR LARGER--

--DAMAGE APPROXIMATION IN THE UPPER MEGA PLUS ULTRA RANGES--

--FIRST CASUALTY ESTIMATES 1.5 BILLION APPROX--

--SECONDARY CASUALTIES X2--

--PLANET-WIDE ENVIRONMENTAL IMPACT AT TERMINAL MINUS 5.5.

-- ESTIMATE FOUR BILLION
CASUALTIES WITHIN SIX MONTHS --

SAM? ARE YOU *HEARING* ME, SAM?

RADIATION BACKWASH HAS BOLLIXED ALL TRANSMISSIONS ACROSS THE SCALE, ROIYA.

BUT SAM *HAS* TO KNOW ZANNI IS SAFE...

"HE HAS TO KNOW AT *LEAST* THAT.

"IT'S *SOMETHING* TO HOLD ON TO."

CHAPTER 23

Thus Far in Scion

What started with a mysterious sigil led to war. Prince Ethan of the West-ruling Heron Dynasty was graced with a mark granting him power, leading to the accidental scarring of Prince Bron of the East-ruling Raven Dynasty during ritual combat.

When the battle was met, first victory belonged to the Herons, but Ethan's oldest brother and heir to the throne, Artor, was brutally slain by Bron. Ethan swore vengeance.

Not long after, Bron was imbued with power by Mai Shen, who revealed herself to him as a member of the godlike First. Bron then murdered his father, framed his sister Ashleigh for the crime, and took the throne for himself.

Ethan confronted Bron in the Raven Keep but was defeated, managing to escape thanks to Ashleigh's help. The Raven princess was, in fact, part of the Underground movement dedicated to freeing the genetically engineered Lesser Races.

Ethan promised his loyalty to the Underground, much to the chagrin of his brother Kai and sister Ylena, who lead the Heron invasion. Ethan and Ashleigh's voyage to the undersea city of Haven in search of a sanctuary for the Lesser Races ended in disappointment. While still in Haven, however, Ethan and Ashleigh gave in to their mutual attraction. Upon their return to the surface, Ethan made plans to take the Tournament Isle as their sanctuary.

Meanwhile, the Heron invasion force was destroyed in an ambush led by Bron. Kai and Ylena barely escaped with their lives.

Ron **marz** Jim **cheung** Don **hillsman II** Justin **ponsor** Troy **peteri**

NEWS?

A BATTLEFIELD TRANSMISSION HAS BEEN RECEIVED FROM THE EXPEDITIONARY FORCE, SIRE.

A GREAT DEAL OF THE MESSAGE WAS *GARBLED*, BUT WE'VE RECONSTRUCTED AS MUCH OF IT AS WE COULD.

IT'S...*NOT GOOD*.

DANE?

THE RAVENS WERE WAITING IN AMBUSH WHEN THE EXPEDITIONARY FORCE PASSED THROUGH THE FELGARD NOTCH.

IT WAS A *MASSACRE*.

THOSE FEW WHO WEREN'T *BUTCHERED* FLED ALONE OR IN SMALL GROUPS.

MARIELLA, THERE'S *NO SIGN* OF KAI OR YLENA.

YOU CAN *SURRENDER* OR YOU CAN *DIE*.

EITHER OPTION IS FINE WITH ME.

I DON'T THINK YOUR MEN ARE LIKELY TO *LAST* VERY LONG...

...BUT I CAN PROMISE *YOU* WON'T BE AROUND TO FIND OUT.

WELL?

SURRENDER. *SURRENDER!*

DROP YOUR WEAPONS!

GOOD CHOICE.

WHAT DO YOU *WANT?*

WHY DID YOU COME HERE, HERON?

JUST BE THANKFUL YOU'RE *ALIVE* AND STOP ASKING QUESTIONS.

LOOKS LIKE YOU PICKED UP A *SCRATCH*, EXETER.

IT'S NOTHING.

PRINCE ETHAN!

IT *IS* YOU, IS IT NOT?

IT IS. YOU ARE THE HERON GARRISON FOR THE ISLAND?

AYE, SIR. WHAT'S *LEFT* OF US.

WHEN THE WAR BROKE OUT THE RAVENS ATTACKED AND *IMPRISONED* THOSE OF US WHO SURVIVED.

STAND BACK...

...I'LL HAVE YOU RIGHT OUT OF THERE.

A MIRACULOUS DISPLAY, SIRE. WE ARE *GRATEFUL*.

WE'VE BEEN LOCKED AWAY AND TREATED LIKE DOGS.

IT'S YOUR *KINGDOM* THAT IS GRATEFUL. YOU'VE DONE YOUR DUTY WITH HONOR, ALL OF YOU.

OUR CAPTORS NEVER SHARED NEWS OF THE WAR, MY PRINCE.

DOES THE CONFLICT *FAVOR* US?

I'M NOT REALLY SURE.

NOT *SURE*, MY PRINCE? WELL, AT LEAST THE *TOURNAMENT ISLE* IS OURS, AND THE RAVENS NOW *OUR* PRISONERS.

NO. I'M AFRAID *YOU'LL* HAVE TO LEAVE THE ISLAND AS WELL.

I'M... NOT SURE WE UNDERSTAND, SIRE.

IT'S OUR *DUTY* TO SERVE OUR KINGDOM'S CAUSE. WE HAVE NO WISH TO BE *RELIEVED.*

YOU *DO* MISUNDERSTAND. YOU'RE NOT *BEING* RELIEVED.

I'VE COME TO THE TOURNAMENT ISLE FOR REASONS HAVING NOTHING TO DO WITH THE *WAR.*

I'VE COME TO CLAIM THE ISLAND AS A *SANCTUARY* FOR THE UNDERGROUND...

...SO THE LESSER RACES HAVE A PLACE THEY CAN BE *FREE.*

BUT...
...YOU CAN'T BE SERIOUS, PRINCE ETHAN. WE ARE AT *WAR*.

YOUR KINGDOM *NEEDS* YOU. YOUR *FATHER* NEEDS YOU, *NOW* MORE THAN EVER.

I'M SORRY. I'VE MADE MY DECISION.

THIS ISLAND NOW BELONGS TO THE LESSER RACES, AND YOU'RE NO LONGER WELCOME HERE.

YOU AND YOUR MEN WILL BE SENT FROM THE ISLAND BY BOAT.

YOU SHOULD REACH HERON SHORES WITHIN A DAY, *LESS* IF THE WEATHER'S WITH YOU.

I CANNOT BELIEVE *LOYALTY* MEANS SO LITTLE TO YOU.

HOW CAN YOU *DO* THIS? HOW CAN YOU *TURN AWAY FROM*—

ENOUGH.

TAKE THEM AWAY, EXETER.

THEM *AND* THE RAVENS, AND PUT THEM ON THE BOATS.

AT ONCE, ETHAN.

TRAITOR.

ARE YOU ALL RIGHT?

WHY WOULDN'T I BE? I WAS NEVER EVEN *TOUCHED* IN THE BATTLE.

AND EVEN IF I *WAS,* THIS THING ON MY ARM WOULD *HEAL* ME, RIGHT?

YOU *KNOW* THAT'S NOT WHAT I MEAN.

IT'S WHAT HAD TO BE DONE. I DIDN'T *LIKE* IT...

...BUT LATELY I FIND MYSELF DOING A LOT OF THINGS I DON'T LIKE.

YOU DID THE *RIGHT* THING.

YES.

I DOUBT ANYONE'S GOING TO GIVE EXETER TROUBLE, BUT I'LL CATCH UP WITH THEM JUST THE SAME.

MAKE SURE THERE ARE NO UNFORTUNATE *INCIDENTS.*

BE CAREFUL, ASHLEIGH.

ETHAN...

...YOU SHOULD BE PLEASED. YOU WERE ABLE TO TAKE THE ISLAND WITHOUT THE LOSS OF A SINGLE LIFE.

WE ACCOMPLISHED *THAT MUCH*, AT LEAST.

THOUGH FRANKLY WE'LL NEED TO ACCOMPLISH *MORE* THAN RUNNING OFF A HANDFUL OF GUARDS FROM A DESOLATE ISLAND.

ANY VICTORY IS WORTH ENJOYING, ETHAN.

I WANTED TO ASK YOU SOMETHING *ELSE*.

YOU AND ASHLEIGH SEEM MUCH *CLOSER* THAN YOU DID BEFORE YOUR JOURNEY TO HAVEN.

DID SOMETHING *HAPPEN* BETWEEN THE TWO OF YOU?

I GUESS YOU'VE KNOWN ME TOO LONG FOR ME TO HAVE MUCH CHANCE OF HIDING SOMETHING FROM YOU, SKINK.

YES, WE'RE *TOGETHER* NOW. I WAS FINALLY ABLE TO ADMIT HOW MUCH I CARE ABOUT HER.

THAT'S GOOD.

I'M GLAD *YOU* THINK SO. I DOUBT YOU'D HEAR MUCH AGREEMENT FROM MY PARENTS.

OR MY BROTHER AND SISTER.

THOUGH I DON'T SUPPOSE I SHOULD REALLY BE WORRYING ABOUT *THEIR* REACTION.

THEY'RE ALREADY GOING TO DISOWN ME FOR BEING A *TURNCOAT*.

I CAN'T MAKE IT MUCH *WORSE* BY BEING WITH THE ENEMY'S SISTER.

I THINK THERE ARE MORE *IMMEDIATE* THINGS YOU SHOULD BE CONCERNED ABOUT.

LIKE HOW WE'RE GOING TO *HOLD* THIS ISLAND WHEN THE KINGDOMS FIND OUT WHAT WE'VE DONE?

BELIEVE ME, THAT *HAS* CROSSED MY MIND.

BEFORE, I ONLY HAD TO CONTEND WITH THE RAVENS BEING AN OBSTACLE. NOW MY *OWN* KINGDOM COULD BECOME ONE.

WE'VE PUT OURSELVES SQUARELY BETWEEN THEM, SKINK.

LITERALLY.

BUT I DO BELIEVE THIS PLAN HAS A CHANCE OF SUCCEEDING.

IF EVERYTHING HAPPENS THE WAY IT'S SUPPOSED TO. AND IF I CAN *RELY* ON THIS POWER I HAVE.

I REALIZE WE'VE DONE THE *EASY* PART BY TAKING THE ISLAND.

KEEPING IT IS GOING TO BE THE REAL TEST.

HAVE FAITH, ETHAN. GOOD *DOES* TRIUMPH.

I'LL GO SEE WHAT KIND OF FOOD STORES ARE LEFT AND PREPARE SOMETHING.

REST.

BOLD COURSE OF ACTION, TAKING A WHOLE *ISLAND* FOR YOURSELF.

NOT FOR MYSELF.

FOR THE LESSER RACES. FOR A SANCTUARY.

THERE'S NO NEED TO SOUND APOLOGETIC. I'VE ALREADY SAID THE CAUSE YOU'RE PURSUING IS A NOBLE ONE.

SLAVERY OF *ANY* KIND IS DEPLORABLE.

NADIA, YOU'VE STAYED WITH US SINCE WE MET...

...EVEN THROUGH SOMETHING *DANGEROUS* LIKE THIS.

YOU'VE STAYED WITH US, AS FAR AS I CAN TELL, WITHOUT MUCH *REASON*.

WE HAVEN'T EVEN HAD A CHANCE TO *TALK*.

SO...

...*TALK*.

ALL RIGHT.

I KNOW SKINK'S TOLD YOU WHO I REALLY AM. WHO MY *FAMILY* IS, I MEAN.

IMAGINE MY SURPRISE TO FIND I'D HAD MY LIFE SAVED BY AN ACTUAL *PRINCE*.

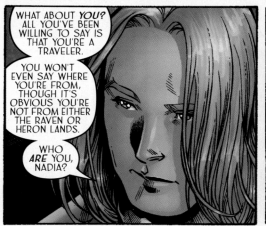

WHAT ABOUT *YOU?* ALL YOU'VE BEEN WILLING TO SAY IS THAT YOU'RE A TRAVELER.

YOU WON'T EVEN SAY WHERE YOU'RE FROM, THOUGH IT'S OBVIOUS YOU'RE NOT FROM EITHER THE RAVEN OR HERON LANDS.

WHO *ARE* YOU, NADIA?

WELL, I HOPE YOU WON'T BE DISAPPOINTED TO LEARN I'M *NOT* A PRINCESS.

I'VE BEEN CIRCUMSPECT BECAUSE I *AM* VERY MUCH A STRANGER IN A STRANGE LAND.

BUT I OWE YOU *HONESTY* AT THE VERY LEAST.

I SAID I WAS FROM FAR AWAY. I MEANT IT.

I'M FROM *TIGRIS*, TRULY THE OTHER SIDE OF THE WORLD FROM HERE.

WE'VE ISOLATED OURSELVES FOR SO LONG, I CAN UNDERSTAND WHY MOST PEOPLE DON'T EVEN BELIEVE MY KINGDOM IS *REAL*.

OUR ANCESTORS WERE *AGAINST* THE FORCED LABOR OF THE LESSER RACES, SO THEY ABANDONED BOTH THE RAVEN AND HERON KINGDOMS.

THEY SET OUT ACROSS THE OCEANS AND FOUNDED THEIR OWN KINGDOM. THEY LABORED FOR THEMSELVES...

...AND EVENTUALLY BUILT *MACHINES* THAT LABORED FOR THEM.

AT LEAST NOW I UNDERSTAND WHY YOU WERE SYMPATHETIC TO THE UNDERGROUND'S CAUSE.

WHY DID YOU *LEAVE* TIGRIS?

RIGHT NOW I'M HELPING *YOU*.

GOOD.

I HAVE A FEELING WE'RE GOING TO NEED IT.

HE LED US STRAIGHT INTO THE TEETH OF THAT AMBUSH, THEN *LEFT US* TO OUR FATE.

RECRIMINATIONS ARE USELESS NOW, BROTHER.

WE NEED TO CONCENTRATE ON GETTING HOME.

TURNED INTO A *MASSACRE* AT FELGARD NOTCH. HEARD MAYBE A FEW DOZEN ESCAPED...

HOLD.

...AND *THEM* SCATTERED ALL OVER THE COUNTRYSIDE. RIGHT RETRIBUTION FOR THE ROUT AT POINT KORDAY.

KING BRON'S PROVEN HIMSELF, AS FAR AS *I'M* CONCERNED. HE'S NOT SQUEAMISH ABOUT *WIPING OUT* THE HERONS...

...UNLIKE HIS *FATHER.*

MAYBE A LITTLE *TOO* ANXIOUS TO WIPE THEM OUT. I'M ALL FOR TAKING THE FIGHT TO *THEM*...

...BUT PUTTING THE WARSHIPS TO SEA AND LEAVING OUR COASTLINE UNPROTECTED, I DON'T KNOW...

YOU HEARD?

I DID.

LET'S GET DOWN TO THE WATERFRONT AND SEE IF WE CAN FIND OUT WHEN—

ANCESTORS.

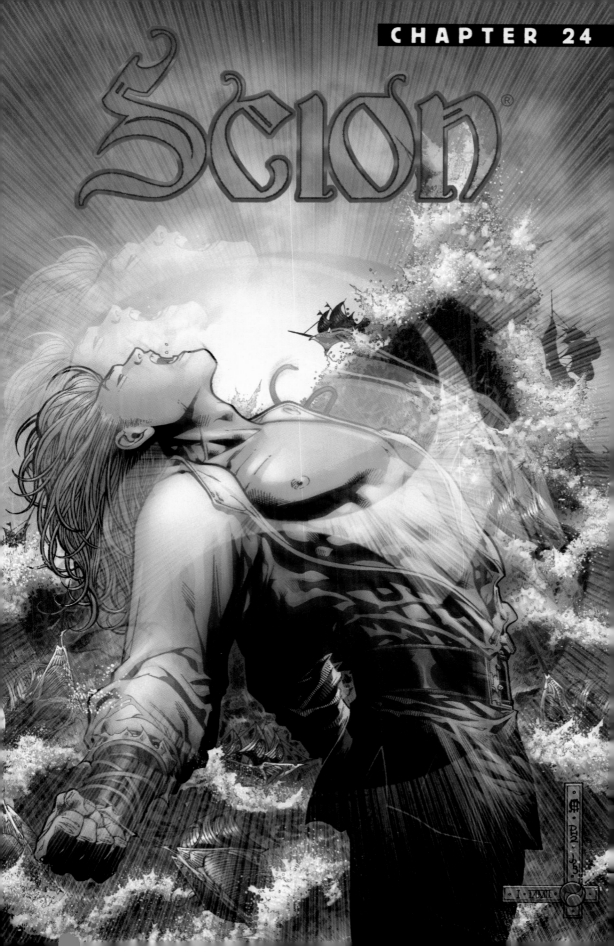

Chapter 24
by

Ron
marz
WRITER

Jim
cheung
PENCILER

Don
hillsman II
INKER

Justin
ponsor
COLORIST

Troy
peteri
LETTERER

ETHAN!

THEY'RE COMING!

WHAT? WHO'S COMING, NADIA?

THE RAVEN FLEET.

I WENT FOR A WALK THIS MORNING, DOWN TO THE DOCKS, AND I SAW THE SHIPS.

STILL FIVE OR SIX LEAGUES OUT TO SEA, BUT DEFINITELY HEADING FOR THE HARBOR.

YOU CAN *SEE* THAT FAR?

I CAN.

THEY MUST BE COMING TO THE ISLAND TO LAY ON SUPPLIES.

THEY CAN'T *POSSIBLY* KNOW WE'RE HERE.

THEY WON'T FIND THEIR GARRISON WHEN THEY COME ASHORE.

WE'LL HAVE TO BE *WELL CONCEALED* IF WE'RE TO HAVE ANY HOPE OF THEM MOVING ON.

IT'S *HIM*...

...AND AT LEAST ONE OF THE RAVEN SOLDIERS WE SENT OFF THE ISLAND.

THE FLEET MUST HAVE PICKED THEM UP.

WHICH MEANS THEY *DO* KNOW WE'RE HERE.

IT WOULD HAVE BEEN BETTER IF THOSE SOLDIERS HAD NEVER LEFT THE ISLAND...IF YOU TAKE MY *MEANING,* ETHAN.

THAT WASN'T A NECESSARY OPTION AT THE TIME, EXETER.

LET'S WORRY ABOUT WHAT WE'RE *GOING* TO DO, INSTEAD OF WHAT WE *COULD'VE* DONE.

IT LOOKS TO BE NEARLY THE ENTIRE FLEET.

BRON MUST BE READYING A WESTERN *INVASION.* THAT'S THE ONLY EXPLANATION THAT MAKES SENSE.

IF HE HAS ENOUGH MIGHT TO INVADE YOUR HOMELAND, WE STAND NO CHANCE OF *HOLDING* THIS ISLAND.

I DOUBT IT'S THE *ISLAND* HE'S INTERESTED IN...

...AS MUCH AS IT IS *ME* AND *ASHLEIGH.*

SHE'S DUE BACK **SOON**, ETHAN.

NOT SOON ENOUGH, SKINK.

AND EVEN WHEN SHE DOES RETURN, DO YOU REALLY THINK IT WILL BE ENOUGH TO HOLD THE ISLAND?

NOT **NEARLY**.

WE'RE LEFT WITH ONE CHOICE. IF IT'S **ME** BRON WANTS, THAT'S WHAT WE'LL GIVE HIM.

THE REST OF YOU CAN CONCEAL YOURSELVES. MAYBE ONCE IT'S SETTLED BETWEEN ME AND BRON...

...**ONE WAY** OR THE OTHER...

...THE FLEET WILL LEAVE.

NO. **THAT'S** NOT A NECESSARY OPTION EITHER.

WE'RE CLOSE TO ACCOMPLISHING THE IMPOSSIBLE. TO MAKING A DREAM **REALITY**.

AND SOME DREAMS ARE WORTH **FIGHTING** FOR.

YOU TAUGHT ME THAT, ETHAN.

THE THREE OF YOU GO PREPARE A SECOND LINE OF DEFENSE, HIGHER UP, NEAR THE ARENA.

WE'LL MAKE THEM **EARN** EVERY BIT OF THIS ISLAND.

EXETER, YOU CAN'T DO THIS **ALONE**. YOU'LL BE—

THIS IS WHAT I AM **BEST** AT, ETHAN.

WHEN THE RAVENS LAND...

...THEY'LL FIND **ME**.

KING DANE...

...THE LONG-RANGE SCOUTS HAVE RETURNED. THEY'RE REPORTING A SIGHTING OF THE RAVEN FLEET...

...AND IT APPEARS TO BE THE *ENTIRETY* OF IT...

...MAKING FOR THE BAY AT THE TOURNAMENT ISLE.

THE *ENTIRE* RAVEN FLEET HAS PUT TO SEA, ADMIRAL?

WITH THAT SORT OF MIGHT BRON OBVIOUSLY PLANS AN *INVASION*.

AYE, SIR. BUT THEY'LL HAVE NO WAY OF KNOWING *WE'VE* PUT TO SEA AS WELL.

THEY'RE LIKELY LOOKING TO TAKE ON SUPPLIES AT THE ISLE.

WE'LL BLOCKADE THE HARBOR MOUTH AND *CRUSH* THEM WHILE THEY LIE AT ANCHOR.

THEY ARE *OURS*, SIRE.

THEN GIVE THE ORDER, SHAYLAH...

...*FULL SPEED* TO THE TOURNAMENT ISLE.

STEP LIVELY, YOU LOT...

...*FAN OUT* THROUGH THE STREETS.

SEARCH EVERY BUILDING, EVERY ALLEY. *FIND* THE KING'S SISTER AND THE HERON PRINCE.

KILL ANYONE ELSE YOU COME ACROSS, BUT *THOSE TWO* MUST BE TAKEN ALIVE, OR YOU'LL ANSWER TO KING BRON HIMSELF.

HE'LL BE ASHORE PRESENTLY, AND FOR *ALL* OUR SAKES, WE'D BETTER HAVE WHAT HE WANTS.

WHAT ARE WE *DOING* HERE? WE SHOULD BE SPILLING HERON BLOOD, NOT RUNNING THE KING'S ERRANDS.

THAT'S THE SORT OF TALK THAT'LL GET YOUR *OWN* BLOOD SPILLED, BOY.

KEEP YOUR MOUTH *SHUT,* AND YOU'LL KEEP YOUR *HEAD* ON YOUR SHOULDERS.

SPOOKY, THIS, SEEING THE TOURNAMENT ISLE DESERTED LIKE—

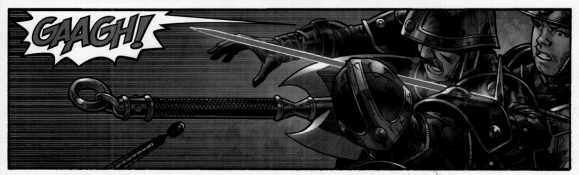

GAAGH!

THIS ISLAND HAS BEEN CLAIMED BY THE UNDERGROUND AS A *SANCTUARY* FOR ALL LESSER RACES...

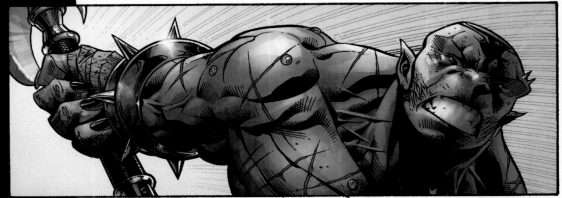

"I SHOULD BE STANDING AND FIGHTING *WITH* EXETER..."

...NOT LEAVING HIM ON HIS *OWN* LIKE THIS.

ETHAN, YOU *KNOW* THIS IS THE ONLY HOPE WE HAVE OF HOLDING THE RAVENS...

...OF *HOLDING OUT* UNTIL ASHLEIGH RETURNS.

BY LETTING EXETER *SACRIFICE* HIMSELF?

THAT'S A HIGH PRICE TO PAY FOR—

BWOOM

WHAT WAS *THAT?*

THUNDER?

NO, IT CAME FROM THE *HARBOR.* IT SOUNDED LIKE...

...CANNON FIRE.

FIRE!

HOW DID THEY *FIND* US?!

THERE'S NO REASON THE HERON FLEET WOULD EVEN BE AT *SEA!*

THIS HAD TO BE A *TRAP*, WITH *ETHAN* AS BAIT. WE'LL BE BOTTLED UP AND BLOWN TO—

CHOOM

SPOOSH

COME ABOUT FOR ANOTHER *BROADSIDE*, THEN WE *CLOSE!*

I *WANT* THAT *FLAGSHIP!*

MORE WATER! HURRY OR SHE'LL BURN DOWN TO THE *WATERLINE!*

SIRE, *LOOK!*

THERE, OFF THE PORT SIDE!

IS THAT *ETHAN?*

WHAT'S HE DOING *HERE?*

WHAT'S HE *DOING?*

I AM A PRINCE OF THE HERON DYNASTY, YET I CAME HERE TO CLAIM THE TOURNAMENT ISLE AS A *SANCTUARY* FOR THE LESSER RACES.

BUT YOUR *WAR* FOLLOWED ME HERE.

LEFT TO YOUR OWN DEVICES, YOU RAVENS AND HERONS WOULD DESTROY *EACH OTHER* AND *ANYONE* CAUGHT IN BETWEEN.

I TRIED TO VIEW THE CONFLICT AS SOMETHING *SEPARATE,* SOMETHING I COULD TURN MY BACK UPON.

I WAS *NAÏVE* TO THINK SUCH A THING. BUT UNDERSTANDING THAT I CAN'T *IGNORE* THE WAR DOESN'T MEAN I HAVE TO *ACCEPT* IT.

I WAS RESPONSIBLE FOR *STARTING* THIS WAR...

...AND *I* WILL BE THE ONE TO END IT!

HOW COULD *HE* COMMAND ENOUGH POWER FOR THAT DISPLAY?

ENOUGH POWER TO *DRIVE* THE FLEETS FROM ONE ANOTHER.

WE MUST... →*KOFF KOFF*←

...*STOP* THIS CONFLICT...

...OR HE'LL DESTROY US.

HOW, DANE?

HOW DID ETHAN *DO* THAT?

I KNEW MY SON HAD BEEN TOUCHED BY GREATNESS...

...BUT I *NEVER* REALIZED HE WAS CAPABLE OF SUCH A THING.

ETHAN?

WHAT...

...WHAT *HAPPENED* TO HIM?

EVERYTHING OUT THERE'S *STOPPED*, SKINK. ETHAN SEPARATED THE FLEETS, THEN...

...*NOTHING.*

HOW WAS THAT EVEN *POSSIBLE*, WHAT ETHAN DID?

IF ETHAN *OPENS* HIMSELF TO THE POSSIBILITY, HE IS CAPABLE OF A GREAT DEAL.

A *GREAT* DEAL.

DO YOU THINK THIS WILL KEEP THE FLEETS AT BAY?

I BELIEVE SO...

...AS LONG AS THEY DO NOT REALIZE SUCH A USE OF ETHAN'S POWER HAS LIKELY *EXHAUSTED* HIM.

EXHAUSTED HIM? THEN...

...WHERE *IS* ETHAN?

The PENNY ARCADIAN

Copiously Illustrated   Afternoon Edition, Price One Penny

CURTAINS FOR DETECTIVE

❧ OUR PLAYERS ❧

SIMON ARCHARD

THE CITY'S FAVORITE SON,
HIS MIND IS RAZOR-SHARP

EMMA BISHOP

A FETCHING BEAUTY,
HER SPIRIT CRAVES ADVENTURE

MALCOLM LIGHTBOURNE

A CUNNING CRIMESMITH
WITH COUNTENANCE UNREVEALED

MURDERED ON STAGE
BEFORE HORRIFIED AUDIENCE

VICTIM PREY TO PRESTIDIGITATION FOUL

CASE SOLVED, SUSPECT AFOOT

To conclude his performance this evening past in a most spectacular and grisly style, visiting stage magician "The Amazing Corradino" unveiled before his shocked audience a human corpse.

According to eye-witnesses, Corradino invited audience member Detective William Wilson to participate in his act, vanishing him within a gimmicked wooden cabinet before the eyes of all present. Moments later, Corradino himself undertook a water-tank escape known as the "Hydrocoffin," but when the tank stood revealed, those present were shocked to see Wilson's corpse floating inside, with Corradino nowhere to be found.

Partington's favorite son, Detective Simon Archard, on the scene and on the trail, located and confronted Corradino within hours but could not effect his capture. Since then, information provided the *Penny Arcadian* suggests that "Corradino" may well be an alias for the brilliant and noted Malcolm Lightbourne, Archard's former partner, believed deceased. Archard himself declined comment on this speculation; however, if Lightbourne has, indeed, returned in some uncanny fashion and has enjoined Archard in adversity, the *Arcadian* will follow such a story closely, as it can only bode ill for the stalwart citizens of

••• **PLEASE CONTINUE INSIDE**

As It May Please the Court and Barristers of Our Fine Land:

WAID
WRITER

GUICE
PENCILER

PERKINS
INKER

DePUY
COLORIST

LANPHEAR
LETTERER

WHAT WERE YOU *DOING* BACK THERE?

EXERCISING THE POWER OF *OBSERVATION.*

BECAUSE IT'S TOO WEAK TO NOTICE A *MOVING* TRAIN?

A LADY CAN*NOT* TRAVEL *WITHOUT* HER *MAKEUP,* SIMON.

HEAVY OR *NOT,* YOU'D BE *SURPRISED* HOW USEFUL THAT CASE CAN BE.

WERE I IN NEED OF AN *ANCHOR...*

TICKETS!

I HAVE OURS RIGHT *HERE,* CONDUCTOR-- THE FIRST OF *MANY* ON THIS JOURNEY.

WE CHANGE TRAINS ONCE?

TWICE. ACCORDING TO MY MOST RECENT *INFORMATION*--

...IT'S NOT AS IF ANYTHING NOTEWORTHY IS HAPPENING *INSIDE* THE CAR.

JUST A *DAY* AGO, SIMON AND I WERE ATTACKED BY A MAN I KNOW ONLY AS *LIGHTBOURNE...*

...SIMON'S FORMER *PARTNER,* BELIEVED *DECEASED.*

WHATEVER LIGHTBOURNE'S *MOTIVES* MAY HAVE BEEN, ONLY *SIMON* KNOWS...BUT THEY CUT HIM TO THE *QUICK...*

...PROVOKING FROM HIM A *STUNNINGLY* UNCHARACTERISTIC... AND *WORRISOME*...SHOW OF *ANGER,* THE MYSTERY OF WHICH I AM DETERMINED TO SOLVE.

AMUSING.

WHEN I PASS OUT FROM *EXCESSIVE LAUGHTER*, DO REVIVE ME.

→HNNNNFF←

WHAT IN THE *WORLD*--?

COSMETICS.

I WAS *UNAWARE* THAT LIPSTICK WAS SOLD BY THE *POUND*.

--THE *GYPSIES* WE SEEK ARE CAMPED OUTSIDE OF A REMOTE VILLAGE CALLED *TELESTROUD*. THAT'S OUR *DESTINATION*.

*A*ND NO MORE IS *SAID*, AT LEAST NOT FOR A *WHILE*. RESIGNED TO *SILENCE*, I CONTEMPLATE THE *SCENERY*. AFTER ALL...

SIMON MITIGATED THE DISAPPOINTMENT OF HAVING LOST LIGHTBOURNE'S *TRAIL* BY INSPECTING THE *KERCHIEF* LIGHTBOURNE LEFT BEHIND...

AMATEUR DEDUCTIONS

...ONE WHOSE UNIQUE *PATTERN* AND STYLE OF *WEAVING* BETRAYED ITS ORIGINS WITH A CERTAIN *GYPSY TRIBE* EXISTING, FRUSTRATINGLY ENOUGH...

...HALFWAY ACROSS THE *CONTINENT*.

...KEEP YOUR BACK *TURNED*, SIMON ARCHARD...JUST ONE SECOND *MORE*...

...FOR *VENGEANCE* IS AT LAST *UPON* YOU... THE VENGEANCE OF--

...LIKE CARRYING AN *ANVIL*...

FWUMP

HHUKKK!

NNNNFF!

BLASTED *CASE!*

WE'LL WIRE THE *OTHERS* FROM THE NEXT TOWN...WARN THEM THAT PRETNARD'S *INITIATION* MET WITH TERMINAL *FAILURE.*

THERE ARE ALWAYS *OTHERS* WHO WISH TO JOIN PARTINGTON'S MOST *EXCLUSIVE* GENTLEMEN'S CLUB...

WHAT'S HE *SAYING?* WHAT SEEMS TO BE THE *PROBLEM* WITH TELES--

DOLSUNOR!

APPARENTLY, THIS TRAIN DOESN'T *GO* TO TELESTROUD.

OSTENSIBLY.

JETE PARNUAN FILHAGRI TELESTROUD. *DOLSUNOR.*

DOLSUNOR?

DOLSUNOR!

Oh, *DEAR.*

THAT'S IT... PAY NO *ATTENTION...*

SIMON, BE *CAREFUL!* YOU DIDN'T *HIT* ANYONE DID YOU?

→HKKK←

DNN'T *SWWLLOW* DNN'T--

→GULP!←

IF *SO,* I'M SURE THEY'D SPEAK *UP.*

→≋←

APPARENTLY *NOT,* THEN.

TSK! TSK!

I *WARNED* YOU PRETNARD WOULD FAIL. *ASSASSINATION* IS A *YOUNG* MAN'S GAME, NIGEL.

OR AT LEAST A *CLEVER* MAN'S. AH, WELL.

BUT IT'S *ON* THE *RAIL LINE!* WHY CAN'T IT--

IT'S NOT THAT IT *CAN'T* STOP. IT *WON'T* STOP.

FOR SOME REASON, EVERYONE ON THIS TRAIN IS UTTERLY *CONVINCED* TELESTROUD IS TO BE *AVOIDED* AT *ALL COST*--SOME NONSENSE ABOUT IT BEING *HAUNTED,* THOUGH I COULD BE *MISTRANSLATING.*

EITHER WAY, WE'LL HAVE TO GO ON TO THE NEXT STATION AND *DOUBLE BACK* SOMEHOW.

OR...

...

Oh, NO. *NO.* NO "OR." THERE *IS* NO "OR," SIMON!

NO "OR!"

IS THAT CLEAR?

NOT REALLY, NO.

AAAAH!

OOOOF!

WHUFF!

UNNGH!

OOOHHHHH

ALIVE... I'M ALIVE...

WHAT WAS THAT?

I SAID, "I'M ALIVE"--

--AND, I MIGHT ADD, PERFECTLY COMPOSED AND ON MY FEET-- UNLIKE A CERTAIN DETECTIVE I COULD--

I BELIEVE THAT WOULD BE YOUR COSMETICS BAG?

IT IS NOT A BURDEN.

♫♫

YOU MAY STOP PRETENDING THAT YOUR LUGGAGE PROVIDES SUITABLE TRANSPORT, EMMA.

♫

I SEE YOU RECONSIDERED YOUR *SEA CRUISE.*

AND ABANDON *YOU?* WHEN THE *COMPANY* IS *SO DELIGHTFUL?*

SHALL WE *WALK,* OR WOULD YOU PREFER TO LEAP AND *TUMBLE* SOME MORE?

ℰXCEPT...

...THERE *ARE* NO VILLAGERS.

IT'S NOT A *GHOST TOWN.* THERE ARE *MANY SIGNS* OF LIFE.

A *CAGED BIRD...*

...A *CHILD'S BALL* BOUNCING DOWN THE STREET...

YOU MIGHT WISH TO APPLY THAT *RAPIER WIT* TO THE PROBLEM AT *HAND*.

PROBLEM?

DETERMINING THE CONNECTION BETWEEN LIGHTBOURNE AND THE GYPSIES IS EASIER *SAID* THAN *DONE*.

WE'LL HAVE TO EARN THEIR *TRUST*... WHICH, DEPENDING UPON THEIR *LOYALTIES*, COULD BE *DIFFICULT*.

YOU'RE RIGHT. I NEVER CONSIDERED THAT THEY MIGHT BE *HOSTILE* TOWARDS US. HAVE YOU A *STRATEGY* IN MIND?

YES.

ASK THE *VILLAGERS* FOR *THEIR* THOUGHTS.

...AND YET...

...NOT A *SINGLE HUMAN BEING* IN SIGHT.

WHAT *NOW?*

WITH THE LIKELIHOOD *DWINDLING* OF AN ENTIRE POPULATION SPRINGING UP, AND SHOUTING *"SURPRISE!"*, I SUGGEST WE FIND A WAY TO APPEASE OUR *APPETITE* AND *FATIGUE*. I TAKE IT THIS IS AN *INN*.

SIMON, WHERE COULD THESE PEOPLE HAVE *GONE?* WHY WOULD THEY *LEAVE?* HOW LONG HAVE THEY BEEN *MISSING?*

DAYS? *WEEKS?*

HOURS. LOOK.

FRESHLY PREPARED FOOD.

FOR *WHO?* SURELY THERE CAN'T BE *GUESTS* UPSTAIRS.

I DON'T ⇒HUFF⇐ SUPPOSE YOU'D ⇒HUFF⇐ BE INTERESTED IN HELPING ME WITH MY--

WHAT DO *YOU* THINK?

THAT ALL I WANT ⇒HUFF⇐ IS TO FIND A WAY ⇒HUFF⇐ TO DROP THIS ON YOUR FOOT.

TRY DROPPING IT IN *THERE,* INSTEAD. CATCH YOUR *BREATH.*

I'LL CONTINUE THE *SEARCH.*

CAN YOU READ THE *SIGN?*

"THE *EMPTY STEIN.*"

FITTING.

SURELY. IN FACT, THE REGISTER SHOWS THAT NO ONE HAS TAKEN A ROOM HERE IN *DECADES.*

HELLO? IS ANYONE HERE?

GATHER YOUR *BAGS.* WE'RE GOING *UP.*

YOU'RE NOT FOOLING *ME,* SIMON. YOU'RE EVERY BIT AS TIRED AS I AM. IT'S BEEN A *VERY* LONG DAY, AND WE--

--WE --

SIMON, DID YOU *HEAR* THAT? THERE *MUST* BE SOMEONE *DOWNSTAIRS!*

OR, MORE ACCURATELY...

BUT -- THE ENTIRE *TAVERN* WAS --

--AND *NOW* --

--AS IF *NOTHING* UNUSUAL HAD --

DO YOU THINK THEY'VE EVEN *NOTICED* US?

NO *NEED*, YOUNG MAN. I RECOGNIZE THE LANGUAGE. IF YOU TALK *SLOW*, I'LL TRY TO KEEP *UP*.

NAME'S *OSGOLD*. TELESTROUD'S... *BURGOMEISTER*, YES?

EXCUSE *KARAN* FOR BEING *STARTLED*. WE DON'T *GET* MANY *VISITORS* HERE.

SHOCKING.

AND WHAT *DOES* BRING YOU TWO SO FAR...OUT OF YOUR *WAY*?

PASSING *THROUGH*. THOUGHT WE'D *REST* FOR THE NIGHT.

...SOME**ONES**.

>GASP<

I **THINK** SO, YES.

WE SHOULD SPEAK TO WHOEVER IS IN **CHARGE**. I SUGGEST YOU **ASK** THEM BEFORE THEY **BEAT** US TO DEATH.

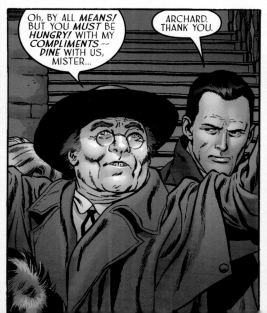

OH, BY ALL **MEANS!** BUT YOU **MUST** BE **HUNGRY!** WITH MY **COMPLIMENTS** -- **DINE** WITH US, MISTER...

ARCHARD. THANK YOU.

IF SIMON EXPECTED HIS NAME TO **MEAN** SOMETHING HERE, HE'S **DISAPPOINTED.** NO ONE REACTS.

SIMON'S **QUIET.** CLEARLY, HIS PLAN IS TO PLAY **INNOCENT** FOR A WHILE...WISELY SOAK **UP** INFORMATION RATHER THAN LOSE PATIENCE AND TIP OUR **HAND.**

SO HOW IS IT WE WALKED INTO A *COMPLETELY DESERTED* VILLAGE THIS AFTERNOON, BURGOMEISTER?

WRONG *AGAIN*.

DESERTED? *TELESTROUD*? WHY I MUST NOT BE AS FLUENT IN THE LANGUAGE AS I *THOUGHT*, YOUNG MAN, IF I HEARD YOU SAY WE WEREN'T *HERE*.

HEH. WISH WE *COULD* JUST *TAKE OFF* AND FROLIC *ABOUT*, BUT THE TOWN CAN'T RUN *ITSELF*.

NO, SIR. MAYBE SOME FOLKS WERE OUT *SHOPPING* OR SUCH...

SIR, UNTIL *FIVE MINUTES* AGO, THE STREETS AND HOMES OF TELESTROUD WERE *TOTALLY EMPTY*. WHERE WERE YOU *HIDING*?

AGAIN -- MR. ARCHARD, IS IT? -- AGAIN, YOU MUST BE *MISTAKEN*. NOW, *PLEASE* ENJOY OUR *HOSPITALITY*.

YOU LOOK *PUZZLED*.

ONLY AT *EVERYTHING YOU DO*. THAT WAS THE MOST UNUSUAL ATTEMPT I'VE EVER *SEEN* AT MAINTAINING A *LOW PROFILE*. WHY DID YOU *CHALLENGE* THE *MAYOR*?

...TAKE IN THE *SIGHTS* AND TELL ME THEY DON'T *BOTHER* YOU. CHURCHGOERS ENTERING A *SERVICE*...

...CHILDREN AT *SCHOOL*... A GREAT DEAL OF *MANUAL LABOR*...

Oh, WE'D *LOVE* TO. IN FACT, WE'D LIKE TO SEE MORE OF THE *TOWN*. YOU WON'T MIND IF WE LOOK *ABOUT*...?

NOT AT *ALL*.

HERE. WE'LL HAVE *HÜGNAR* ESCORT YOU.

WE WON'T REQUIRE AN ESCORT.

I *INSIST*.

I'M SURE YOU *DO*. VERY WELL.

BECAUSE WE WOULDN'T BE IN ANY LESS DANGER HAD I *NOT*--

--AND BECAUSE *STAYING* WOULDN'T HAVE HELPED US FIND OUR *GYPSIES*.

NOW, DO YOU MIND DETERMINING HOW FREE WE ARE TO *SPEAK*?

SO *I'VE* AN IDEA, HANDSOME. WHY DON'T YOU AND I GO FIND OURSELVES A NICE, QUIET *HAYSTACK*?

PULSFOR ACH *NUGEN*?

NOT A WORD. BUT HE THINKS *YOU'RE* CUTE.

SO *NOTED*. NOW...

IT SEEMS TERRIBLY *LATE* FOR THAT SORT OF ACTIVITY, BUT PERHAPS THAT'S HOW THESE PEOPLE *LIVE*.

THEN AGAIN, *WHO* FISHES AT *NIGHT*?

MY POINT PRECISELY.

RATHER THAN ASK THE TOWNSPEOPLE ABOUT THE *GYPSIES*-- SINCE THE LESS THEY KNOW OF OUR *MOTIVES,* THE *BETTER*--

--I NOW PREFER TO ASK THE *GYPSIES* ABOUT THE *TOWNSPEOPLE.*

AND WE'LL COME ACROSS THEM *WHERE*...?

ALMOST CERTAINLY ENCAMPED NEAR THE *RIVER.* THIS WAY.

TENDING THE *FIELDS* BY *MOONLIGHT.* IT'S POSITIVELY *EERIE* AND--

<STRIKE *FAST! HEADS* AND *HEARTS!* TAKE *THEM!*>

THE *GYPSIES.* WHAT ARE THEY *YELLING?* THREATS?

--SIMON!

<THERE THEY ARE!>

MORE LIKE *PROMISES.* GOOD *LORD,* SIMON...IT'S A *MASSACRE!*

OSSGOLD! OSSSGOLLD!

THEY WON'T FIGHT *ALONE* FOR *LONG.* OUR *TOUR GUIDE'S* OFF TO WARN THE *TOWN.*

SIMON, WHAT HAVE WE STUMBLED *INTO?* I'LL *TRANSLATE* AS BEST I *CAN,* BUT...

"UNHOLY *WHAT?*"

"I--I'M NOT *CERTAIN.* ALL I KNOW IS THAT THE FARMERS ARE *ARMED*--

"--AND THE TIDE OF BATTLE HAS QUICKLY TURNED IN THEIR *FAVOR!*"

AAAAGGHH!

<BY HELL *ITSELF!* WE KNEW NOT OF THEIR *WEAPONS!* RETREAT, I SAY! *RETREAT*--FOR NOW!>

<BUT MARK MY *WORDS,* YOU *GHOULS*--WE WILL RETURN, AND WHEN WE DO→>

SIMON? SIMON, WHERE ARE YOU *GOING?*

<GIVE THEM *BACK!* GIVE US BACK OUR *DAUGHTERS!*>

<YOU HAVE *STOLEN* THEM FOR YOUR *UNHOLY RITES!*>

<RETURN THEM --

--OR FACE OUR *VENGEANCE!*>

<BROTHERS, TO *ARMS!* NOCK YOUR *BOLTS* AND LET *FLY!*>

<--WE SHALL *FREE* OUR YOUNG WOMEN FROM THE CLUTCHES OF THE *UNDEAD*-- OR *DIE TRYING!*>

AND THESE ARE THE VAGABONDS WITH WHOM WE HOPE TO STRIKE A *PEACEFUL DIALOGUE?* SIMON, THEIR *FEROCITY*--

WAIT. "*UN...DEAD?*"

THE *VILLAGERS.* THEIR ABSENCE IN *DAYLIGHT*... THEIR NOCTURNAL *PROWLINGS*...

EVEN...EVEN *MYTHS* HAVE *SOME* BASIS IN *FACT.* SIMON, COULD THESE PEOPLE ACTUALLY...

...ACTUALLY *BE VAMP*--

TO STOCK UP ON *GARLIC* AND *WOODEN STAKES.*

REALLY?

NO.

YOU DON'T HAVE TO BE *SMUG* ABOUT IT.

HAVE WE BEEN *INTRODUCED?*

⇒SIGH⇐

POINT *TAKEN.* SO WHERE *ARE* WE GOING?

BACK TO THE *INN.* EARLIER, I NOTICED SOMETHING *PECULIAR* IN THE *KITCHEN* THAT WOULD EXPLAIN *MUCH* --

WE DIDN'T ASK FOR ROOMS.

NONETHELESS, YOU CAN'T *POSSIBLY* BE *SURPRISED* THAT THEY'RE BEING "*OFFERED.*"

SO WHAT DO WE DO *NOW?*

TRY TO GET SOME *REST* -- BUT LOCK YOUR *DOOR* AND SLEEP *LIGHTLY.*

BUT WHAT IF THESE PEOPLE *ARE* VAM--

DONE.

<OH, HÜGNAR...IT'S SO *DARK* IN HERE... CAN YOU *GUIDE* ME...?>

*S*UCCESS. THE MOMENT WE'RE OUT OF LINE OF *SIGHT,* I HEAR SIMON'S DOOR *CLOSE...*

-- AND IF MY SUSPICIONS ARE CORRECT, I SHOULD BE ABLE TO FIND --

ENJOY YOUR LITTLE *TOUR*, MR. ARCHARD?

OH!

FORGIVE THE SPARSE *RECEPTION*. HÜGNAR ALERTED US TO THE...*COMMOTION* NEARBY. IT'S BEING...*HANDLED* BY THE TOWNSFOLK.

SUCH *EXCITEMENT*. YOU MUST BE *EXHAUSTED*. HÜGNAR WILL SHOW YOU TO YOUR *ROOMS*, FRESHLY *MADE*.

SWEET *DREAMS*.

DON'T WASTE MY TIME MAKING ME LISTEN TO THE REST OF THAT SENTENCE.

PLAY *ALONG*. DEMONSTRATE *COOPERATION* FOR THE BENEFIT OF OSGOLD'S LACKWIT *THUG*.

WE WANT HIM TO REPORT TO OSGOLD THAT WE'RE TUCKED SAFELY *AWAY* FOR THE NIGHT.

WHEN, IN FACT...

...YOUR IMMEDIATE TASK IS TO MAKE CERTAIN HE TAKES HIS EYES OFF OF *ME*.

...BUT I'VE NO DOUBT HIS ROOM IS *VACANT*.

I'VE NO *NOTION* WHAT IT IS HE'S *SEARCHING* FOR...

Chapter 8
by

Mark
WAID
WRITER

Butch
GUICE
PENCILER

Mike
PERKINS
INKER

Laura
DePUY
COLORIST

Dave
LANPHEAR
LETTERER

DAYLIGHT? HOW CAN THERE BE--

→SIGH← BECAUSE I FELL ASLEEP, THAT'S HOW. SO MUCH FOR KEEPING MY GUARD UP.

...AS INDICATED BY THE COMPLETE ABSENCE OF PEOPLE.

WHEN SIMON AND I STUMBLED INTO THIS TINY BURG YESTERDAY, NOT A SOUL WAS AROUND. THE STREETS AND BUILDINGS WERE UTTERLY DESERTED. ONLY AFTER DUSK DID THE NATIVES APPEAR...

SIMON?

LUCKILY, NO HORRIBLE FATE BEFELL ME IN THE NIGHT. I'M GREETED BY ANOTHER BRIGHT MORNING IN THE SMALL HAMLET OF TELESTROUD...

...THOUGH WHEN SIMON ACCUSED THEM OF HIDING, THEY DENIED EVERYTHING... CLAIMED WE WERE "MISTAKEN."

WE'RE--

YOU'RE THE WIVES AND DAUGHTERS OF THE GYPSY TRIBE CAMPED NEAR THE RIVER.

HOW DID YOU--?

DURING THE BROAD LIGHT OF DAY, MYSTERIOUS UNSEEN FORCES DRAGGED YOU AWAY AND TO THIS DUNGEON UNDERNEATH THE INN.

CAN YOU TELL ME WHY?

SO THE LOCAL MEN COULD... COULD...

...COULD MATE WITH US.

NO SIGN OF HIM ANYWHERE. I KNOW HE ELECTED TO *INVESTIGATE*...

...WHICH MEANS HE'LL RETURN ANY MOMENT TO TELL ME HOW HE UNRAVELED THE WHOLE MYSTERY CLUED ONLY BY A *BROKEN SHOELACE* AND *A MELON RIND*.

NNNNFF! ALL RIGHT. SO MY COSMETICS CASE *DOES* HAVE A RATHER ELEPHANTINE *HEFT*. THERE. BUT IT'S AN ADMISSION I'LL TAKE TO MY *GRAVE*.

MEANING I'D RATHER *DIE* THAN ENDURE ANOTHER ORATIM FROM SIMON REGARDING ITS *USELESSNESS*...

BEST TO PUT ON MY *FACE*, THEN. NO POINT IN APPEARING IN PUBLIC BOTH BEFUDDLED *AND* BLEMISHED--

AND THAT COMPLETES THE *PUZZLE*. THE TOWNSFOLK ENSCONCE THEMSELVES *HERE* BETWEEN DUSK AND DAWN, YES?

YES! RESTING NEAR THEIR *NATIVE SOIL* SO THEY MAY *ROAM* AND *FEED* BY THE *MOONGLOW*-- AS *VAMPIRES DO*!

INDEED. THEIR FANGS SHARPENED BY *LEPRECHAUNS* WHILE THEY RIDE THEIR *UNICORNS* TO THE MOON.

VAMPIRES ARE THE STUFF OF *FICTION*. MY INTERESTS LIE *SOLELY* IN *FACT*.

THE TELESTROUDIANS *DO* HIDE FROM *SUNLIGHT*, THAT MUCH IS *PLAIN*. I'VE A THEORY *WHY*...BUT I'LL HARDLY *PROVE* IT FROM IN *HERE*.

HOW DID YOU *FIND* US?

EARLIER, I SAW A NUMBER OF COVERED DISHES IN THE KITCHEN *UPSTAIRS*--

--SIMPLE MEALS THAT I *DIDN'T* SEE BEING SERVED IN THE *TAVERN*--

--YET HAD TO HAVE BEEN PREPARED FOR *SOMEONE.*

ONCE I *HEARD* THE *GYPSIES* LAMENT OVER THEIR *ABDUCTED WOMEN*... ...THE CONNECTION WAS OBVIOUS.

FOLLOW ME, AND *HURRY.* YOUR CAPTORS WILL RETURN TO DEAL WITH ME *DECISIVELY*--

WHICH MEANS *SOMEONE* WILL TALK TO ME.

IT'S NOT MY IMAGINATION. DESPITE OUR BUILDING QUITE THE INVESTIGATIVE *RESUMÉ* TOGETHER, SIMON, A MAN ORDINARILY AS WARM AS A *COBRA* AND TWICE AS *TALKATIVE,* IS TRUSTING ME LESS...NOT *MORE.*

HE *MAINTAINS* HIS SATURNINE COUNTENANCE AS REGARDS HIS FORMER PARTNER, *LIGHTBOURNE.* I THINK I'VE BEEN EXTRAORDINARILY *PATIENT* WAITING FOR INFORMATION ABOUT THE MAN GIVEN THAT HE CAME AFTER ME WITH AN *AXE.*

A *THEORY* ABOUT SIMON'S BEHAVIOR IS BEGINNING TO TAKE SHAPE INSIDE MY OWN HEAD, BUT THAT'S A MATTER FOR *LATER.*

FLOORBOARDS--! SOMEONE'S COMING!

SIMON, MY POWDER...!

AND TO THINK HOW YOU CATERWAULED ABOUT MY COSMETICS. SORRY NOW?

YES.

SORRY I HIRED AN ASSISTANT WHO GLOATS.

I QUITE BEG TO DIFFER. SO MUCH MYSTERY IN TELESTROUD... HOW BEST TO SHED LIGHT ON IT?

PERHAPS WE WALK OUTSIDE? SUCH A LOVELY, SUNNY DAY...

NO! NO! I--

YOU WILL VERIFY MY CONCLUSIONS.

WE'LL BE DEALING IN THE RELATIVELY NEW SCIENCES OF GENETICS AND ATOMIC MATTER, SO TRY TO FOLLOW.

THE TELESTROUDIANS POSSESS A PECULIAR-- AND RATHER SEVERE-- PHOTOSYNTHETIC DERMAL CONDITION.

SOMETHING AKIN TO ALBINISM?

MARGINALLY... BUT FAR MORE DRASTIC.

LIKELY ITS ORIGINS LIE IN SOME SORT OF SPONTANEOUS MUTATION...BUT GIVEN A VILLAGE THIS REMOTE, A CENTURY OR SO OF INBREEDING COULD EASILY DRIVE A RECESSIVE GENE TO FULL DOMINANCE.

HELPLESS?

BUT WHY DO YOU *STEAL* US FROM OUR *BEDS?* DO YOU HOLD US SOMEHOW *RESPONSIBLE* FOR THIS CONDITION?

ON THE *CONTRARY*, MY DEAR...IT'S YOU WHO'LL *SAVE* US.

EVERYTHING MR. ARCHARD SAYS IS *TRUE*...BUT THERE IS *MORE*. DESPITE OUR *PRAYERS*, WITH EACH GENERATION, OUR SENSITIVITY *INCREASES*. THE CONDITION *WORSENS*.

OUR ONLY HOPE IS TO BREED IT *OUT*, BUT WE CANNOT... WITHOUT *FRESH BLOOD*.

AND GATHERING WOMEN FROM NEIGHBORING *TOWNS*...

...WAS *IMPOSSIBLE*. THERE *ARE* NO "*NEIGHBORING TOWNS*," MR. ARCHARD.

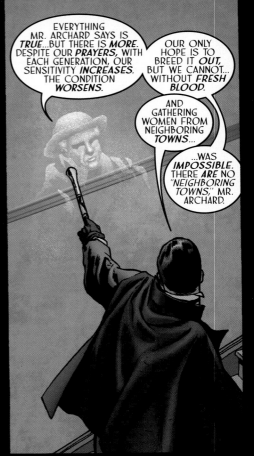

WITH SO LITTLE LIGHT REACHING THEIR *EYES*, THEIR SIGHT IS BADLY, THOUGH NOT IMPOSSIBLY, *LIMITED* --

--WHICH IS WHAT FORCES THEM UNDERGROUND BY DAY INTO THE ONE ROOM IN TOWN BUILT DEEP ENOUGH TO FULLY *SHIELD* THEM.

WHO SAYS THEY'VE GONE *ANYWHERE?*

I'VE BROUGHT A FEW *WITH* ME. THE *REST?*

AS I SAY, THEY CAN'T ENDURE *MUCH* TRAVEL... BUT IF IT'S A MATTER OF EXTERMINATING *PESTS...*

...WELL, THEY CAN *CERTAINLY* MAKE IT AS FAR AS A *GYPSY ENCAMPMENT...*

=HHGGKKK--!

EMMA!

IF YOU'VE *HURT* HER, I *SWEAR* --

--I'LL *NEVER* HEAR THE *END* OF IT!

*N*OT ANOTHER WORD IS *SPOKEN.*

WE'VE NO *TIME* FOR *REPARTEE.* WE HAVE TO WARN THE *GYPSIES* OF THE UPCOMING *ATTACK.*

GUIDED BY THE *WOMEN*, WE THUNDER TOWARDS THEIR CAMP AT *BREAKNECK SPEED* --

HOW *TOUCHING.* I SEE QUITE A FUTURE FOR YOU IN *CHARM SCHOOLS.*

TEACHING?

ATTENDING.

YOU SAID OUR ATTACKERS' VISION WAS *LIMITED?* MIGHT I SUGGEST--

--THAT A *FLASH CHARGE* MIGHT BLIND THEM *ALTOGETHER.*

AAAAH!

CAN'T *SEE*--

MY *EYES! MY EYES!*

GO! HURRY! HURRY!

--AND *ARRIVE*--

--*TOO LATE.*

THE GYPSIES ARE UNDER *FULL SIEGE* -- AND BY WHAT, THEY'VE *NO IDEA.*

DESPERATELY, THEY *LOOK* FOR *SOME-THING* TO HIT.

TELL THEM TO *FOLLOW ME!*

TO *WHERE?* HOW DO WE EVEN *KNOW* WE'RE *RETREATING?*

FASTER! WE'RE ALMOST *THERE!*

WHAT? SIMON, I CAN BARELY *HEAR* YOU! THE *WATERFALL*--!

EXACTLY.

ENTER SIMON.

<YOU! YOUR PEOPLE DID THIS! OUT COMES YOUR HEART, YOU DAMNABLE->

<FATHER, NO! HE'S NOT FROM HERE! HE SAVED US!>

<FROM WHAT? DEATH IS THE WIND ITSELF! OUR BROTHERS FALL MURDERED! HOW CAN WE FIGHT THIS SORCERY?>

HE SAYS--

I CAN GUESS!

THIS WAY!

WH-- SIMON, WHAT ARE YOU SUGGESTING? DO WE JUMP?

NO.

NOW!

ATTACK!

BEAUTIFUL. IN ONE STROKE, THE TABLES ARE *TURNED.* THE VILLAGERS' ONLY REAL WEAPON WAS *SURPRISE.* TAKE THAT *AWAY...*

<YOU DARE COME AFTER US? WE MEANT YOU NO HARM→>

THEY'RE FLEEING! TO THE WAGONS AND AWAY WHILE THEY GATHER THEIR WOUNDED!

THERE'LL BE NO PURSUIT! ISN'T THAT RIGHT, BURGOMEISTER?

FOR NOW, MR. ARCHARD...FOR NOW. BUT THERE *WILL* BE RETRIBUTION... NO MATTER THAT IT TAKES A LIFETIME.

THE SUDDEN WINDWHISPER, THE GHOSTLY FOOTFALL... SOMEDAY, WHEN YOU LEAST EXPECT IT...

...THAT WILL BE US. THIS, I SWEAR.

WONDERFUL. HOW DO I NOT WORRY ABOUT *THAT* FOREVER?

BY CONTINUING TO CARRY A COSMETICS BAG WITH ITS OWN GRAVITATIONAL FIELD.

LET'S GO.

isn't enough...

FORGE

RGE

MONTHLY COMICS FOR YOUR BOOKSHELF

You owe it to yourself to try FORGE, the other half of CrossGen's Compendia™ Series. With five distinctly different stories serialized every month in full color, it's a big fat book at an unbeatable price. Available everywhere CrossGen Comics are sold.

CROSSGEN COMICS

Graphic Novels

THE FIRST 1	Two Houses Divided	$19.95	1-931484-04-X
THE FIRST 2	Magnificent Tension	$19.95	1-931484-17-1
MYSTIC 1	Rite of Passage	$19.95	1-931484-00-7
MYSTIC 2	The Demon Queen	$19.95	1-931484-06-6
MYSTIC 3	Seige of Scales	$15.95	1-931484-24-4
MERIDIAN 1	Flying Solo	$19.95	1-931484-03-1
MERIDIAN 2	Going to Ground	$19.95	1-931484-09-0
MERIDIAN 3	Taking the Skies	$15.95	1-931484-21-X
SCION 1	Conflict of Conscience	$19.95	1-931484-02-3
SCION 2	Blood for Blood	$19.95	1-931484-08-2
SCION 3	Divided Loyalties	$15.95	1-931484-26-0
SIGIL 1	Mark of Power	$19.95	1-931484-01-5
SIGIL 2	The Marked Man	$19.95	1-931484-07-4
SIGIL 3	The Lizard God	$15.95	1-931484-28-7
CRUX 1	Atlantis Rising	$15.95	1-931484-14-7
SOJOURN 1	From the Ashes	$19.95	1-931484-15-5
SOJOURN 2	The Dragon's Tale	$15.95	1-931484-34-1
RUSE 1	Enter the Detective	$15.95	1-931484-19-8
CROSSGEN ILLUSTRATED Volume 1		$24.95	1-931484-05-8